'What Do You Want, Brad?'

'That's a strange question to ask, Caryl,' he said and moved to study her dainty figure in its négligé and matching robe.

'I'm tired . . . and I'd rather be alone, if you don't mind.'

'It so happens that I do mind!'

She had no time to steel herself for what was to come before his arms were about her, and her lips were crushed beneath the mastery of his.

ANNE HAMPSON
currently makes her home in England, but this top romance author has travelled and lived all over the world. This variety of experience is reflected in her books, which present the ever-changing face of romance as it is found wherever people fall in love.

Dear Reader:

During the last year, many of you have written to Silhouette telling us what you like best about Silhouette Romances and, more recently, about Silhouette Special Editions. You've also told us what else you'd like to read from Silhouette. With your comments and suggestions in mind, we've developed SILHOUETTE DESIRE.

SILHOUETTE DESIREs will be on sale this June, and each month we'll bring you four new DESIREs written by some of your favorite authors—Stephanie James, Diana Palmer, Rita Clay, Suzanne Simms and many more.

SILHOUETTE DESIREs may not be for everyone, but they are for those readers who want a more sensual, provocative romance. The heroines are slightly older—women who are actively involved in their careers and the world around them. If you want to experience all the excitement, passion and joy of falling in love, then SILHOUETTE DESIRE is for you.

I'd appreciate any thoughts you'd like to share with us on new SILHOUETTE DESIRE, and I invite you to write to us at the address below:

Karen Solem
Editor-in-Chief
Silhouette Books
P.O. Box 769
New York, N.Y. 10019

ANNE HAMPSON

Devotion

Published by Silhouette Books New York

America's Publisher of Contemporary Romance

SILHOUETTE BOOKS, a Simon & Schuster Division of
GULF & WESTERN CORPORATION
1230 Avenue of the Americas, New York, N.Y. 10020

Distributed by Pocket Books

ISBN: 0-671-57155-9

First Silhouette Books printing June, 1982

10 9 8 7 6 5 4 3 2 1

Map by Tony Ferrara

America's Publisher of Contemporary Romance

Printed in the U.S.A.

Other Silhouette Books by Anne Hampson

Payment in Full
Stormy Masquerade
Second Tomorrow
The Dawn Steals Softly
Man of the Outback
Where Eagles Nest
Man Without a Heart
Shadow of Apollo
Enchantment
Fascination
Desire
Realm of the Pagans
Man Without Honour
Stardust
A Kiss and a Promise

Devotion

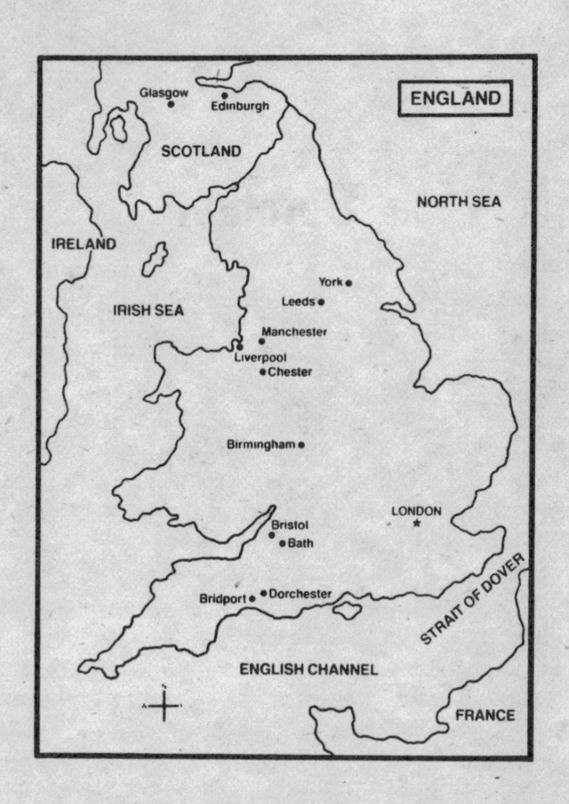
ENGLAND
Glasgow
Edinburgh
SCOTLAND
NORTH SEA
IRELAND
IRISH SEA
York
Leeds
Manchester
Liverpool
Chester
Birmingham
LONDON
Bristol
Bath
Bridport
Dorchester
STRAIT OF DOVER
ENGLISH CHANNEL
FRANCE

Chapter One

The little cottage occupied by the two sisters stood in a secluded clearing on the fringe of the grounds where the main kennel block was situated. Caryl had been with Sandy, trying in vain to pacify him and eventually coming away from his cage with tears in her eyes.

'He'll die of a broken heart,' she predicted on joining Emma, who was in the kitchen preparing the evening meal. 'Just think, he's never before been parted from the invalid lady who's owned him for over twelve years, and now he's to be kept in quarantine for six whole months.'

Emma sighed and nodded her dark head. 'He's in a terrible state, bewildered and wondering what's happening to him and where his beloved mistress is. Apparently he was used to sitting beside her wheelchair all day and sleeping at the foot of her bed at night.'

'And now he's not only parted from her but he has

concrete under him and wire mesh all around his small cage. If only we were allowed to take these quarantined dogs for walks it wouldn't be so bad. They have no real exercise for six months—it's inhuman!'

'You do feel strongly about it, I know.' Emma gave another sigh. She was dicing carrots and dropping them into a pan of hot, salted water. 'I fully agree that the dogs should be allowed exercise, but unfortunately it's the rule that they are confined to their small cages for six months, and there isn't a thing we can do about it.'

'I'd go over to Sandy later this evening, but Mrs. Blakeman'll scream if she sees me.' Mrs. Blakeman was the proprietor's wife, and from the first Caryl had had difficulty in getting along with her. Caryl was too soft-hearted for the job, the woman had said. The dogs suffered a little, but there were few casualties. That was true, Caryl had to admit, seeing as there had been only two deaths in the kennels in eight years.

Caryl was quiet over dinner, her mind wholly occupied with the little dog who was pining for his mistress. He had been collected from Heathrow Airport three days ago and had been crying ever since. Caryl had charge of him, along with a number of other dogs, and it was only after sustained persuasion that she had managed to get him to take a drink of milk. As for food—he had not eaten anything since being put into the relatively small cage which was the regulation size as set down by the Ministry of Agriculture for dogs undergoing quarantine.

'I've a good mind to risk Mrs. Blakeman's temper and go over to see Sandy,' said Caryl thoughtfully as she began to wash the dishes. 'She can't eat me, and in any case, it won't be the first time she's had complaints to make.'

'If only you could be a little harder, love.' Emma sighed as she picked up a tea towel to dry the cutlery. 'I sometimes wonder if we made a mistake in taking on this kind of work.'

'We both love animals; that was reason enough.' There had been another reason, though, for when their father had remarried, his new wife and daughters had found it impossible to share the same house. The opening for kennel-maids was advertised, and as there was a cottage going along with the jobs, the girls applied. Two girls were required, preferably with experience. Mr. Blakeman had taken one look at them and decided experience was not necessary. He had known they would work conscientiously and would be kind to the animals in their care. They had instantly become friendly with Mr. Blakeman, and Emma managed to get along reasonably well with his wife, but for some reason Caryl and her employer's wife seemed invariably to rub one another the wrong way, and if it had not been for inconveniencing Emma, Caryl would have sought a post at another kennels.

It was a fortnight later that Caryl said with relief, 'Sandy seems to be settling down a bit better now.'

'Due entirely to you,' stated Emma emphatically. 'The time you spend with him! He couldn't help but respond to that kind of petting and pampering. His mistress ought to remember you in her will!'

'She'll probably never know just how much trouble her little dog has caused,' laughed Caryl. It was Sunday, and although she and Emma were off duty, Caryl had been over to see Sandy and give him his midday snack. 'He's actually managing to wag his tail now and then.'

'Success! I think you're marvellous, Caryl.' Emma's

voice was edged with admiration, and her eyes, too, were admiring as they swept over Caryl's face, taking in the delicately fashioned features, the wide, compassionate mouth above an unexpectedly determined chin, the small, retroussé nose, the smoky blue eyes framed by long, curling lashes. The brows were exquisitely arched, the forehead high and clear; the hair, russet brown spangled with gold, was short and naturally curly, giving her face an elfin quality which in turn made her appear much younger than her twenty-four years.

The following morning a letter arrived for Emma, and so engrossed did she become in it that Caryl, watching her intently, wondered whom it could be from.

At last Emma glanced up, her face a study as she said, 'You'll never guess who's writing to me.'

'I haven't the faintest idea.'

'Brad Craven.'

'Brad!' Caryl's eyes widened to their fullest extent, then became shuttered. 'What does he want?' So calm the tone, but the forward leap of her emotions set Caryl's nerve ends tingling, her heartbeat racing.

'You'll remember he's the heir of a wealthy landowner in the south of England?'

Caryl nodded. Although time had erased the pain she had once experienced, there was still little about Brad Craven that she did not remember. 'In lovely Dorset, it was.'

'That's right. Sir Geoffrey Goudham is Brad's uncle. I met him each time Brad took me down there, and although he's an overbearing, choleric old man, there was something likable in his makeup. Brad had no parents, and his uncle had adopted the role of guardian.' Emma stopped and grimaced. 'Brad wasn't exactly thrilled with the idea, but he admired the old man, and in effect they seemed to be very good friends.' Another pause, during which a sort of sadness crept into Emma's face. 'Sir Geoffrey's almost blind, and in addition he feels instinctively that he hasn't much time left to live. Brad says he has a young man in attendance on him, a sort of male nurse–companion, who is with him almost constantly.'

'Does Brad still manage the home farm and estate?' Caryl was puzzled as to why Brad was writing to her sister, but she refrained from asking because she knew Emma would tell her in her own good time.

'Yes—well, he doesn't mention it but I expect the position is the same now as when I was engaged to Brad.' Emma's eyes dropped to the letter again. 'If you remember, the old man sent for me after I broke off the engagement. He thought the sun shone out of me and was bitterly disappointed at my action in deciding not to marry his nephew.'

Caryl nodded her head reflectively. 'I remember your telling me about his disappointment and his repeated efforts in trying to make you change your mind.' Memories and impressions came crowding into Caryl's mind, and even now, after six years, she could blush at Brad's treatment of her when, at eighteen, she had thrown herself at him. Losing patience, he had taught her a lesson, in his own arrogant and masterful way, laughing in her face after the humiliating chastisement had been administered.

'The reason for this letter is that Sir Geoffrey told Brad to ask me to go down and see him. Brad wrote to Father to see if I was still there. Dad gave him this address.'

'Shall you go?' Caryl watched her sister intently; she had often wondered if Emma had ever regretted her action in breaking off her engagement to Brad.

'I suppose I ought to, but I can't say I really want to. It's a long way, and, to tell the truth, I'd feel embarrassed, in a way, with Sir Geoffrey being blind. Besides, the fact that I'm not married might set him off again.'

'About Brad, do you mean? So Brad isn't married, either?' It was strange how, after that initial leap of emotion, she could now discuss Brad with total impartiality and lack of any deep feeling. Time, the inevitable healer, had certainly cured her of whatever it was she had felt for Brad. At the time it had seemed like real love that would last forever, but now Caryl believed it was no more than a schoolgirl crush on the inordinately attractive young man to whom her sister had soon become engaged. Whatever it was, it no longer mattered; Caryl felt nothing stronger than interest in this latest and unexpected situation in which Emma had become involved.

'Brad doesn't actually say he isn't married, but I can tell by the gist of the letter that he's still single.'

'You ought to go,' said Caryl. 'The old man won't badger you to marry Brad, simply because he must know that after all this time there could be nothing between you. He probably believed you'd be married to someone else, in any case.'

'Could have done. Father will have told Brad that I'm still single, but whether or not he mentioned Patrick is another matter—and not important.'

'It seems to me that Sir Geoffrey's reason for wanting you to go is that he feels he must see you before—before he dies.' Caryl frowned as she spoke. She was feeling sad at such a request and, strangely, was wishing she had known Sir Geoffrey. He seemed nice in spite of the irascible ways he used to have—and which he probably still had. Caryl fell to wondering about this young man who looked after him. It must be a dull life, and she assumed the man must be a dedicated kind of person to take on a post like that.

'When Sir Geoffrey does die, then Brad'll be a near millionaire—lord of the manor. However, I don't expect his life-style will change much. Brad's dedicated to the outdoor life, to managing the farm and the rest of the estate.' Emma paused in thought, and Caryl did not interrupt her. 'I don't want to go,' she repeated at length, and she looked at Caryl long and hard, a strange expression on her face.

Caryl had fallen into a reflective mood, recalling her first meeting with the man who had later asked Emma to marry him. It was at a dance to which she and Emma had been invited by their father's employer, who was giving it for his staff. Caryl had been drawn to Brad Craven the moment she was introduced to him, and for the whole of the evening she had followed his tall, impressive figure with her eyes, hoping he would dance with her . . . willing him to do so. She had been bitterly disappointed when, although giving Emma a great deal of attention, she realised he hadn't even noticed she had a sister. Afterwards he had remained in her thoughts for a long while, and even now she could recapture his image completely—the finely chiselled features and bronzed skin, tight and clear and stretched so tautly over the prominent cheekbones that hollows were created beneath them to give his features an angular aspect that to Caryl was both attractive and repelling. A formidable face of strength and character, inordinately distinctive owing to the arrogant lines, the steely depths of eyes the colour of deepest grey. The wide, sensuous mouth was yet set and firm, complementing the dominant chin and outthrust jaw. Caryl remembered the tall, lithe frame, and the way Brad walked, with that superior, confident gait that set him apart from all other men in her eyes. She saw him as a typical English gentleman, a man of the patrician class, of the aristocracy . . . and knew instinctively from the start that he was far out of her reach. But yet he had become attracted to Emma, had wanted to marry her.

Caryl had watched with aching heart the affair develop, had known that Brad had a domineering personality and that the woman he married would have to accept that he was her master. She had wondered about Emma and how she would react, for Emma was no weakling, no suppliant who would be happy to be domineered over. He had become a regular visitor to the Chapman home, and although it was Emma who drew him, Caryl would be quite unable to refrain from seizing every opportunity of making sure he noticed her, and one day when she was alone with him she had deliberately flirted, flaunting her attractions in a gauche and inexperienced way which was bound to exasperate him, although of course Caryl did not know that at the time. For a while he managed to ignore her, but then, losing patience, he had spanked her hard and told her to grow up. Caryl felt she hated him, but on the day her sister became engaged to him she wept as if her heart would break.

At the time Emma had admitted it was Brad's expectations which attracted her more than the man himself. He would be much too bossy for her, she had told Caryl. 'I fancy myself as the lady of the manor,' Emma had confessed quite openly, 'and that's why I've accepted him, and yet . . .' A brooding, doubtful silence had followed before Emma added, 'He'll domineer over me, Caryl, and I don't know how I shall react.'

After an engagement lasting two months Emma decided to break it, not at the time realising how that was to affect the old man who had looked forward eagerly to the time when he would have her in his home, bringing it warmth, and producing an heir to follow Brad when the time came.

'I want you to know I'm heartbroken over this,' he had told Emma when, after he had sent for her, she had obeyed his summons and travelled down to Dorset to see him. 'There's no girl I'd rather have for a niece-in-law than you, dear. Won't you reconsider?'

'We're not really suited,' Emma had explained as gently as she could. 'Brad's so arrogantly superior where women are concerned. It's plain that he considers us the weaker sex, and his wife would never be allowed to forget it.' Emma had paused, but the old man just sat there, lost in a sad silence, tears glistening in his eyes. 'I just know I'd rebel, Sir Geoffrey. I could never tolerate being mastered.'

Caryl had heard of the break with mixed feelings, for by then she had almost convinced herself that, once Brad and Emma were married, she would be able to forget how she was feeling for him, simply because she would have to accept that he was lost to her forever.

'I think you should consider going, Emma. It will give Sir Geoffrey pleasure.'

'I'm not sure. You see, if he should ask me anything about myself—what I've been doing with my life—I'd have to mention Patrick, telling Sir Geoffrey I'm engaged. That might make him sad rather than give him pleasure.' She looked inquiringly at Caryl, inviting some comment, and again Caryl noticed that odd expression in her eyes.

'I don't think there's any need to mention Patrick. You could just tell Sir Geoffrey about your job here, and that you and I share a cottage. No, I can't see any necessity for mentioning Patrick.' Caryl allowed her thoughts to dwell for a space on Emma's fiancé. He was in Nigeria for two years, working for an oil company in Lagos, and although he would dearly have loved Emma to have married him before he went so that she could go with him, he at the same time admitted that Nigeria was not the sort of place to start their married life. And in any case, Emma, always wise before the event, had already decided to wait until his stint was done. He would be sent to Holland next, and Emma knew she could be happy there.

'In any case,' she had said, with both Caryl and Patrick present, 'I couldn't leave Caryl on her own. I'm hoping she'll find herself a husband in the next two years.'

Caryl often hoped she would be fortunate enough to meet a man who was her ideal and get married. But no one had come her way, and although she was only twenty-four, six years younger than Emma, she was beginning to resign herself to spinsterhood. When she mentioned this to Emma, her sister would laugh and say she was far too attractive ever to be left on the shelf.

'One day, my love,' she predicted, 'you'll be swept right off your feet!' She had paused and then, quietly: 'You once liked Brad, didn't you?'

Caryl had coloured up. It was the first time her feelings for Brad had been referred to, and in spite of the blush she was able to look at Emma without embarrassment and say, 'At that time it was far more than liking, Emma. It seemed like the real thing.'

'But now you know it wasn't.' More a statement than a question, and Caryl nodded in agreement.

'Yes, it was nothing deep, because there's no pain now.'

'I've been thinking—' Emma's words brought Caryl from her reverie and she looked across at her, feeling rather tense for what appeared to be no reason at all. 'Why don't you go down and pretend to be me? It would be a nice little trip for you, because Brad says the first-class fare will be paid. If Sir Geoffrey's almost blind, he'll not know the difference. We're the same height and colouring—'

'Emma, you're not serious!' Caryl could only gape at her for the next few seconds. 'Why on earth have you suggested a thing like that? And in any case, what about Brad? What would he have to say about it?'

'He'd probably be as casual as I am about it. Old Sir Geoffrey would be happy, so what has it to do with Brad?'

'You're crazy!'

'Well, I can't see what makes you say a thing like that.' Emma frowned almost plaintively. 'It's so happens that I don't feel like making the long journey. It also happens that you are concerned about the old man—'

'Not particularly concerned,' Caryl broke in to deny, 'but I do feel you have the chance of giving him a little pleasure, so you ought to put yourself out to do so.'

'You make me feel so selfish,' complained her sister. 'To tell the truth, I don't think I want to meet Brad again after all this time.'

'You feel you might find yourself regretting the broken engagement?'

Emma shook her head vigorously. 'In no way would I ever come to regret it. I'm in love with Patrick, and that's that. However, I have a feeling I'd be awkward, embarrassed, meeting Brad again. But if you went—'

'I have no intention of going,' interrupted Caryl in a firm, decisive voice. 'If you don't want to go, then you'll have to phone Brad and tell him so.'

It was only a few hours after Emma had phoned that, coming as a shock to everyone concerned, Mr. Blakeman announced that he was closing the kennels down.

'He and his wife are parting,' one of the other kennel-maids said. 'They've had one unholy row, and she's leaving today.'

'When are the kennels to be closed?'

'Very soon. Mr. Blakeman wants to go out to his married daughter in Sydney, Australia.'

'But what about the dogs?' Caryl's thoughts were already with Sandy, who, were he to be moved away from her at this time, would undoubtedly die of a broken heart. His age was against him; the vet had said this right at the start, when it seemed the little dog would never stop fretting.

'The owners will be asked to find alternative accommodation for their pets, but, meanwhile, I believe Mr. Blakeman's already arranging with the owners of Frogholme Kennels to take them.'

'Frogholme!' cried Caryl, going pale. 'No, he can't do that! At least, he can't do it to Sandy. They're the worst quarantine kennels in the country, and in addition they're so far away I'd not even be able to visit

Sandy. They're ten miles beyond Hindlington, which is about sixty miles from here.'

'Well, as far as I know, that's what's going to happen. Why don't you ask Mr. Blakeman yourself, if you're so concerned about Sandy?'

Mr. Blakeman verified what the kennel-maid had said. 'You and Emma will be able to stay at the cottage until you find somewhere else,' he added. 'I shall make that quite clear to whoever buys the land.'

'Can't the kennels be sold as a going concern?'

'It would take time. I want to leave almost immediately. I've had over twenty years at keeping kennels, Caryl, and I'm now eager to retire.' He walked away before Caryl could say anything about Sandy, and she was almost in tears when she entered the cottage after having spent over an hour by Sandy's cage.

'What's wrong?' Emma looked at her with both perception and concern. 'It's the dog, isn't it?'

'He'll die, Emma.'

'I agree, but what can we do?' Emma paused a moment. 'We're all out of work, Caryl. We'd be better thinking of ourselves rather than one little dog, unfortunate as the poor little mite is.'

Caryl suddenly became thoughtful. 'If I remember rightly, Sir Geoffrey owns a quarantine kennels.'

Emma's eyes widened. 'Yes; he established one a few years ago in the grounds of the dower house, which lies a short distance from the main mansion.' A small, perceptive silence followed before Emma said, a trace of humour in her voice, 'You've changed your mind about going on that visit to Dorset?'

'If I could get a job there, and take Sandy with me . . .'

'Why don't you telephone Brad? I have the number on the letter.'

'What about you—if I did succeed in getting myself taken on at the Goudham Kennels?'

'Don't worry about me, Caryl. I shall stay on here, in the cottage for a while—and in any case, I can't see these kennels closing down immediately. The transfer of the dogs will take time; I'm not so sure that Mr. Blakeman can move them without consulting the owners, who will surely want to find alternative kennels for themselves. I firmly believe it'll be a few weeks before all the dogs are rehoused, and in the meantime my job's safe simply because we kennel-maids will be needed. Mr. Blakeman's upset, remember, and he believes he can get out within days. When he calms down a bit, he'll see it's stupid even to think of ridding himself of his encumbrances in such a short space of time.'

'But eventually,' persisted Caryl. 'Where will you go when the kennels do close down?'

'Get another job—or at a pinch I could go out to Patrick.' Something in her voice made Caryl look sharply at her.

'You want to go?'

'The prospect isn't as daunting as it appeared at first. From Patrick's letters Nigeria doesn't seem all that bad. Patrick's gone shares with another man in buying a boat, and they go sailing every weekend. He says the sailing there's just fabulous.' Emma paused in thought. 'You know how keen I've always been to have a boat but didn't think I'd ever be so lucky. Well, here's my chance!'

'You'd not go just for the sailing, surely?'

'Of course not. I want to get married.'

'So if I do land this job with Sir Geoffrey, it'll help you as well?'

'Now don't go getting ideas that I've been making a sacrifice—thinking entirely of you, being on your own here. It's suited me to stay in England because I really believed it wasn't going to be pleasant in Nigeria. From Patrick's last two letters it seems that both he and I were wrong and that one can enjoy oneself there. So just you do your own thing, and I shall be perfectly all right, I promise you.'

Caryl was satisfied. She felt optimistic about getting a job with Sir Geoffrey—or with Brad, because of course it was he who ran the estate, and she supposed the kennels were under his control, too. She might just feel slightly embarrassed at seeing Brad again, especially if he should remind her of that punishment he had inflicted. However, that was a minor concern in comparison with the plight of Sandy. And it was Sandy she was thinking of when she made her final decision to go down to Dorset.

Chapter Two

The noble façade of Goudham Manor shone with a sort of theatrical splendour in the amber glow from the setting sun. Caryl had booked in for one night at an hotel immediately upon her arrival in Dorchester by train from the north of England. After a quick wash and change of dress she took a taxi to Bridport, an attractive little holiday resort with a harbour that was invariably crowded with fishing boats and pleasure craft no matter what time of the year. Goudham Manor occupied a unique position on a knoll about a mile from the resort and was completely surrounded by the extensive farmlands and woodlands that comprised the estate of Sir Geoffrey, the last of a long line of Goudhams who had owned the manor and demesne lands for more than three hundred years.

The taxi crunched to a stop on the loose shingle of

the forecourt, and Caryl felt her legs weaken beneath her as she alighted from the back seat after the driver had opened the door for her. She had made the appointment by phone, and Brad had sounded friendly and interested in her request, a circumstance which gave her both hope and courage. But now, with the meeting imminent, she was trembling, and her stomach muscles felt as if they had tied themselves into tight little knots.

'You want me to wait, miss?' the driver asked as she opened her handbag to pay him.

'No, I don't think so. I might be a long time.'

'Well, if you do want me, just ring the hotel. I spend hours waiting there, so it's most likely the porter'll get me.'

'I shall certainly do that,' she promised.

The car drove off, but Caryl felt as if her feet were glued to the ground, so difficult was it for her to move them. But the door behind her swung open, and she turned to look up into a face that had altered little, the few changes being the lines of maturity which added to his attraction, and the mouth, which seemed rather more full than Caryl had remembered. The dark hair was sprinkled with threads of iron grey at the temples, and all in all the picture she saw was one of nobility and distinction and superlative self-confidence. By contrast Caryl felt small and unsure of herself—a nobody, a mere mortal beside a god! A smile touched her lips because of her thoughts; Brad, who had appeared to have been taking in every detail of her face before his eyes had slid the full length of her figure to absorb her slim beauty, saw her smile and responded as he held out his hand.

'So you managed to get here on time, then? You should have accepted my offer of a lift from the railway station.'

'I didn't want anyone to be waiting. The railway office gave me the impression that all trains run late on Sunday because repairs to the lines are done then.' He had her hand; she felt the pressure of long brown fingers against a ring she wore and felt as if he had broken the skin, so strong was his handshake.

'Come on in, Caryl. You're looking extremely well and beautiful.'

She coloured adorably and was glad of the activity of entering the hall and of Brad's closing the door behind her. She soon found herself in a large, elegant drawing room where the predominating colours were blue and gold. Drapes and carpet were blue, the walls gold. The furniture was antique, wonderfully cared for. The chairs were built for both beauty and comfort, and Caryl sank into one with a sigh on her lips. The train journey had been long and tedious, and the hard seats had not helped. She leant back, crossed her legs, and tried to appear totally at her ease.

'Where's your luggage?' inquired Brad as if he had just thought of it.

'I booked in at an hotel in Dorchester—the Angel.'

'That won't do." He frowned. 'I'll have it brought here.' He was standing close to her chair; she caught the pervasive and lingering smell of aftershave and realised he had changed for dinner.

'I suppose it would have been better if I'd left the visit till the morning,' she said. 'It's getting late . . .' Her voice was silenced by the lift of his hand. She suddenly felt inadequate and lacking in the self-confidence she had meant to assume.

'Not at all.' Brad took the jacket she had taken off and laid it over the back of a chair. 'Can I get you a drink?' He was walking towards a bell-rope by the white marble fireplace. 'What hotel did you say?'

'The Angel.'

A manservant came in response to the summons. 'Have someone take the car and bring Miss Chapman's suitcase from the Angel in Dorchester. The account will be settled later,' he added, and the man nodded and went out. Caryl found herself smiling at the imperious way in which Brad had taken over, not caring if she had any objection to staying here as his guest. Emma would have been furious at behaviour like that and would certainly have made some protest.

'What are you drinking?' Brad was at the cocktail cabinet, his head turned towards her, his eyes flicking over her, taking in what she wore. She felt glad she had changed from her travel-worn dress into one of coral-coloured jersey—very fine and fitting where it ought to fit, and with the skirt full and fairly short. The matching jacket now over the back of a chair was loose-fitting yet exceedingly smart. Caryl had always felt that the ensemble was one of the best buys she had ever made.

'I'll have a dry sherry, please.'

It was brought over to her, and a small antique table placed at her elbow. She expected Brad to move—hoped he would do it quickly because he overpowered her, with his height and his air of superiority. But he did not move; he stood looking down at her with interest, as if comparing what he saw to what she had been as a girl of eighteen. A quirk of amusement caused her to blush and hope he would not remind her of that occasion, would not speak his thoughts aloud.

'You've grown up' was all he said, but even that spoke volumes, and her colour deepened.

'It's been six years,' she said. 'Of course I've grown up.'

'How is Emma?' Unemotional the tone; it was plain that he now regarded her sister as nothing more than a onetime acquaintance.

'She's fine. I suppose she answered your letter?'

'No, but she telephoned shortly before you did. We had a long conversation, and she told me she's engaged to be married.' A small pause, and then, reflectively: 'She'll be thirty now. Wasn't in any hurry, obviously.' Brad walked away to pour himself a drink.

Caryl asked about his uncle. 'We were sorry to hear about his sight,' she added, reaching out for her glass.

'It's very sad, but he is almost eighty. It's a good age.'

'Emma said she had the impression from your letter that he feels he hasn't much longer to live.'

'He's had a couple of minor heart attacks.' Brad moved to a chair and sat down. 'Dinner will be served in about half an hour,' he said, changing the subject. 'It's late this evening because I held it off so that you could join me.'

'That was good of you,' she said shyly. She was right in line with one of the high windows, and the gold of evening touched her face and hair. Brad seemed interested, but only in a superficial way.

'Let us talk about this job you are hoping to get. I see no reason why you shouldn't come here and bring this dog you spoke of.'

'Thank you,' she said swiftly. 'Oh, thank you very much, Brad! You have no idea what it means to me!'

'To you, or the dog? From what I learned from

Emma on the phone, you are more interested in his welfare than in your own.'

She laughed. 'It must sound crazy to you, but as a matter of fact it's very important that Sandy is not parted from me until he goes back to his owner, an invalid lady who adores him as much as he adores her.' Caryl went on to tell him the whole, even though she guessed he knew it all anyway—what with Emma's conversation on the phone and then her own. 'I shan't be able to travel with him, but once he's here and sees me he'll be all right.'

'You might be able to travel with him,' returned Brad thoughtfully. 'If I employ you at once, then you could be the handler.'

'Of course! I'm delighted!'

'Well, that's settled, then. When do you hope to bring this Sandy down here?'

'I believe I could come almost at once. I'm not quite sure about the regulations regarding a situation like this, but it obviously has happened before.'

'Of course. Owners sometimes take a dislike to the kennels first chosen and decide to change.'

'It was a surprise to me to learn that your uncle had kennels. I remembered he did have them, though, and so the idea of asking you for a job came to me.' Caryl was fast gaining confidence, mainly because of the way Brad was with her—friendly and chatty and with a smile now and then. She felt comfortable and knew a tinge of excitement at the prospect of having dinner with him—alone.

'He's an animal lover, and at the time he conceived the idea of a kennels he'd been visiting a quarantined dog with a friend of his and was most unhappy at what he saw. He had visions of providing large quarters for the dogs but soon realised he was under orders from the Ministry of Agriculture. They lay down the rules, and so, whatever idealistic schemes you have, you might as well forget them.'

'You sound as if you're a dog lover, too.'

'I like all animals—except foxes and tigers,' he added with a grimace. 'I don't happen to have a dog in the house at present. Uncle's spaniel died a few weeks ago, and all we have now are the farm dogs. We have three of those.'

'It's going to be most enjoyable for me, working here.'

'You'll be over at the kennels,' he corrected quietly. 'You can live in the dower house. We've turned it into apartments to house some of the farm workers and also two kennel-girls who share the top flat. You can have a small, one-bedroom flat on the ground floor.' Brad paused a moment, and as she looked at him Caryl had the odd impression that he was searching for words with which to say what was in his mind. It seemed a most strange impression to get, simply because hesitancy of that kind was entirely out of keeping with his strong, dynamic personality. When at last he did speak, it was to make a suggestion: would she pose as Emma and meet his uncle the following day? Caryl's mouth parted, but she caught back the exclamation and just stared at him for several seconds in absolute silence.

'It wouldn't be possible,' she began when he interrupted her.

'Why not? Emma told me on the phone that she had suggested you take her place and come down to see Uncle. She saw no problems, because of Uncle's failing sight. He'd never know the difference.'

'Not briefly,' Caryl agreed, but she went on to

remind him that the present situation was different: she would be here to stay.

'You'd not be seeing Uncle after the first meeting tomorrow morning. The kennels are some distance from here, and as Uncle never leaves his room now, he wouldn't even know you were employed at the kennels.'

'Surely he'd know eventually,' persisted Caryl, but Brad was shaking his head.

'He never leaves his room,' he repeated. 'There is no possible way in which he could know you were here.'

Caryl hesitated, but not for long. There seemed to be no snags that she could see, not after she had accepted what Brad had just said.

'Well . . . if you are quite sure, then, yes, I'll pretend to be Emma, just for tomorrow.'

'Thank you,' said Brad with the trace of a smile. 'I was upset when Emma refused to come. Uncle had seemed so sure she would, and his disappointment would have been exceedingly great. I have no idea why he suddenly wanted to see your sister again after all these years, but the doctor seemed to think it would do him a great deal of good if he did see her, and so I wrote to Emma, feeling that even if she were married she'd still come down, just to help my uncle—' Brad broke off and shrugged his shoulder. 'She obviously felt the journey was too much, and that's fair enough—'

'Don't get any wrong ideas about Emma,' Caryl was forced to break in and say. 'She'd do anything for anyone, but it just so happened that when your letter came she wasn't in the mood for a tedious train journey lasting several hours.'

'But you were willing to make it.'

'For Sandy's sake and for that of his mistress. I don't

want Miss Haldene to lose her little pal if I can help it. . . .' Caryl's voice drifted away to silence as she noted his expression. It was one of amusement not untinged with admiration, and when he spoke there was a strange gentleness in his tone.

'It's all very commendable, Caryl, and I don't know what made me hesitate in asking you to do me the favour of posing as Emma. I ought to have known you'd be willing to do it.'

Flattered by his words, Caryl coloured and smiled and on the whole felt awkward and embarrassed. She reached for her sherry and took a sip, glad of something to do which would appear cool and natural. The entry into the room of the manservant was another help. Dinner was served, he said and withdrew.

'This is lovely!' Caryl was exclaiming a few minutes later as she sat opposite her host at a table which, she suspected, could be extended to more than treble its present size. 'Do you dine in here every night, all alone?'

'To be alone is restful after a long day either outside or in my office. I usually have music— Perhaps you would like some now?' He did not wait for her reply but rose from his chair to insert a tape of light classical music into the recorder. The music flowed at once, flooding the room softly, relayed through no fewer than four speakers, each unobtrusively placed in a corner. Caryl closed her eyes, feeling content and happy and faintly excited. But there was no emotional reaction to being alone with Brad in this romantic atmosphere. On meeting him a short while ago after six years she had felt a trifle surprised that her heart had not been stirred, if only in some small way. Was she disappointed at her total lack of feeling? Her smile had been thin, she remembered, thin and polite in a face she knew was undisturbed by troublesome memories. Brad spoke; she opened her eyes and they smiled at him.

'Where are your thoughts?' he had asked quietly.

'I was thinking of our meeting, after six years,' she began, unable to find any means of prevaricating, because she was sure he would know if she were to tell a lie.

'And?' His dark eyes registered interest, curiosity, and just the merest hint of amusement to betray the fact of his remembering the chastisement he had meted out to her.

'One never knows quite what to expect.' She was thinking of Emma and her assertion that she would feel awkward with Brad, embarrassed.

'You must have known you'd be welcome. I believe I made that clear over the phone.'

'You'd already had the idea of my posing as Emma?'

Brad nodded at once. 'I wanted to cheer Uncle up if it were at all possible.' Brad paused and frowned, then added after a reflective silence, 'He's a changed man from the one Emma knew. His warm and happy smile is gone.'

Caryl said without thinking, 'Emma used to say he was bad-tempered at times.'

'Absolutely true,' with a wry grimace. 'I had to have the patience of Job in those days. But he changed a great deal; seemed happy and content for two or three years until his sight began to fail. That depressed him, and he was always going back—reminiscing. I feel that could be the reason why he wanted to see Emma.'

'He wanted to recapture old times?'

'Could be.' Brad fell silent as the first course was being served, and when the man had gone Brad told

Caryl his name was James and he had been his uncle's butler for over thirty years.

Caryl looked down at the plate of smoked salmon and said thoughtfully, 'You mentioned in your letter to Emma that your uncle has a manservant, a sort of male nurse who is with him all the time.'

'That's right. Uncle keeps to his room, as I mentioned, and Robert is with him for most of the time. He's an excellent man who's dedicated to the work he has chosen to do in life. He reads to Uncle; he looks after his clothes and serves him his food. Uncle has a bedroom next to his sitting room, and Robert has one adjoining it. We had a communicating door put in so that Robert can go in to Uncle if he needs him during the night.' Sober the tone and faintly sad. 'I wish Uncle could resume his daily strolls— He used to be fond of walking around the grounds, and sometimes he'd make it to the kennels. But his health has gradually deteriorated, and now he seems unable to walk any farther than to the bathroom or to his bedroom and back.'

'It's all very sad.'

'But your visit will buck him up. I'll see Robert in the morning, and we'll take you in to Uncle when he's washed him and given him his breakfast. Uncle doesn't get up until around half past nine.'

'You spend time with him, of course?'

'Quite often I make time during the afternoon. He retires at eight every night, so I have only a few minutes with him in the evenings.'

'It's a lot for Robert to do on his own.'

'A relief comes in for two evenings a week, which gives Robert the chance of a little recreation.'

'He doesn't have a day off?'

'It's been offered him over and over again, but he

won't take it. As I said, he's dedicated to the work he's chosen to do.'

Caryl looked at Brad across the table, saw the admiration that had entered his eyes. 'This Robert must be exceptional,' she said at length.

'We think so, and we've been most fortunate in finding him. He took to Uncle from the first, and he has certainly made a great difference in his life. We had a succession of female nurses, but they all seemed to treat the job of caring for Uncle as a paid duty, and one which they stuck to to the letter, which meant they would fret and fume if the relief happened to arrive late. Robert doesn't seem to mind if he never gets a break from duty. And that's surprising, because he's only a young man.'

'He's on call for twenty-four hours a day, then?'

Brad nodded. 'Except when he has those two evenings off.'

'He mustn't have a girl friend.'

'Not that I know of.'

The second course arrived, and for a few minutes the two were silent, watching it being served. Afterwards they chatted between pauses when they listened to the music. For Caryl it was a pleasant evening, unmarred even by the glimpses of the past which would now and then flit across her mental vision. That schoolgirl crush had certainly been intense, she thought wryly as she recalled impossible dreams and idyllic fantasies, visions tender and immature, and finally the panic of impending hurt. The pain would never fade, she had told herself at that time, yet here she was, dining with the man concerned and feeling nothing more than a superficial friendliness and the background awareness that he would soon be her employer.

Following the delicious meal there was coffee in the drawing room, served with mint chocolates and liqueurs. At a quarter to ten Caryl felt her eyelids begin to droop and heard her companion say, 'It's been a long day for you, Caryl. Don't hesitate if you want to go to bed.'

'I would like to go,' she returned, faintly apologetic in spite of his assurance. She had not yet been shown her room, and Brad rose at once to ring the bell. A trim maid entered, her glance curiously unfathomable as she looked at Caryl.

'Miss Chapman will be staying the night, Louisa. I expect James told you to prepare a room?'

'Yes, sir, he did.'

'Then please take Miss Chapman to it.'

'Thank you.' Caryl gave him a smile, then tried to suppress a yawn. 'Good night, Brad—' She stopped, arrested by Louisa's keen interest. Was it because she had used Brad's Christian name?

"'Good night, Caryl. Sleep well.'

Louisa preceded her through a massive hall towards a balustraded staircase leading up to the principal bedrooms and suites. Caryl had been given a large, elegantly furnished room, with a bathroom off it. The view was to the sea, where at this time a myriad of lights flickered along the waterfront, while out towards the dark horizon more lights could be seen—just a few—from fishing boats which would be out there until the morning when the catch would be brought in and sold in the little makeshift shops which lined the harbour.

'Is there anything you would like?' asked Louisa, who had already turned the bed covers down. 'The bathroom is in there.' She flicked a finger, indicating a door. But her eyes were restless and still curious, and Caryl had the impression that a question hovered on the girl's tongue but she dared not depart from the formality which her employer would expect of her.

'There's nothing, thank you,' replied Caryl, again suppressing a yawn.

'Would you like tea in the morning?'

'That would be most acceptable.'

'What time would you like me to bring it?'

'About eight o'clock, please.' Caryl watched the girl depart and then wondered if Brad would expect her to join him for breakfast, and if so, what time did he usually have it. However, as the maid had gone and as she felt ready to drop, Caryl decided to forget tomorrow and concentrate on getting into bed in the least possible time. Her suitcase was on a chair; she took out her nightdress and toilet bag and went into the bathroom. Ten minutes later she was between the cool sheets with the haziness of sleep closing in to rob her mind of all clear thought.

Chapter Three

Caryl had no idea what she expected when she entered the large, sunlit room occupied by Brad's uncle. Emma had once described the old man as tall and aristocratic, with dark eyes and strong, noble features. The man sitting there in the tall, high-backed armchair seemed so small as to be almost shrivelled. His glazed eyes were light rather than dark; his face was lined like a detailed map of some intricate drainage pattern. His lips were blue and dry, and the strong chin Emma had mentioned had obviously receded.

Caryl was taken to him at a quarter past eleven, Brad having previously prepared him by explaining that although Emma had arrived the previous evening, it had been too late for her to come in for a chat. She had already been introduced to Robert, whom she took to on sight and who seemed to take to her. Tall and slim, with good-looking features and light brown hair, he gave the impression of being more at home in an office than in caring for an aged man who demanded every hour of his time. He left immediately after Brad brought Caryl in, and Brad himself soon left.

'So you took pity on an old man and came to see me.' The voice was thin, the pale eyes misted and staring, and it was as if their owner were desperately straining to see what she looked like. 'You're just a blur, dear, but I can imagine your lovely face, because you won't have changed much. Tell me, Emma, just what you've been doing with yourself all these years. Tell me why you haven't married before now.'

She hesitated, remembering Brad's warning to be on her guard the whole time. His uncle might be feeble in body, but he was certainly not feeble in mind.

'I haven't yet met the man I'd like to marry,' she offered, answering his second question while mentally studying the first. She and Emma had for the most part lived very similar lives, but for the first two years after the broken engagement Emma had moved around a good deal, and there had been a period of over a year when she worked as nanny to a family in Portugal. Caryl decided not to mention that; in fact, she decided to give Sir Geoffrey a résumé of her own life rather than that of her sister.

'You're thirty, Emma, dear, so it's time you settled down and raised a family. It can be a lonely life without children. I know, because I remained a bachelor, and if it hadn't been for Brad, where would I have been now? I'd have had no one of my very own.'

'One day, Sir Geoffrey, I shall meet the man whom I shall fall in love with and marry.'

'Brad was meant for you, child.'

She bit her lip. This was what Emma had feared.

Caryl said gently, 'It wasn't as simple as you seemed to think. Two people must have a great deal in common for a marriage to succeed. At that time my— I felt unable to go through with the engagement—I didn't want to marry Brad, and I now believe he thanks me for what I did.'

'Why hasn't he married in all this time?' A petulant note had entered the feeble voice which brought it to a slightly higher pitch.

Caryl was frightened in case he excited himself and she injected a soothing tone into her words as she said, 'He, too, will meet the right one, Sir Geoffrey. You wouldn't want him to make a mistake and be unhappy, would you?'

'No, I'd not want that,' he admitted, 'but I had always hoped to see little ones running about here. Goudham is made for children, Emma. Wouldn't you have liked to be brought up in a wonderful place like this?' He was peering again, and even though Brad had assured her he could not see, she knew a tinge of fear that he would grasp the fact that he was being duped.

'Yes, I'd have been very happy if this had been my home as a child.'

'It could be the home of your children, Emma.'

Automatically she shook her head. 'Brad wouldn't want me now, Sir Geoffrey. As I have just said, I am sure he now thanks me for giving him up.'

'But it's very strange that neither of you has ever married.'

'Shall we talk of something else?' she asked with gentle persuasion. 'Tell me about the farm, and the kennels,' she added swiftly. 'Tell me what made you decide to establish a quarantine kennels here at Goudham.' She knew the story, of course, for Brad had told her, but she was hoping to divert him from the tricky subject of the broken engagement.

He began to talk, to tell her how the idea for the kennels came about. She listened attentively; then she talked about herself and what she had been doing for the past few years. Time passed quickly, and the earlier subject had not been reintroduced by the time Robert came to say that Sir Geoffrey's lunch was ready.

'I'm sorry to cut short your chat,' he said with a swift smile, 'but Sir Geoffrey's had enough excitement for the time being.' His voice was apologetic but firm; Caryl rose at once and held out her hand to Sir Geoffrey. His was icy cold, and on impulse she bent to kiss his cheek.

'Goodbye,' she said. 'Have a nice lunch.'

'What time are you going back home?'

'Five o'clock this afternoon. I'll be home at about half past eleven tonight.'

'Be careful, then, dear, and come in to see me before you leave.'

'If Robert says I can.' She looked questioningly at him, and he nodded his head. 'Just for a few minutes,' he agreed, then walked to the door to show her out. There was no nonsense about him, thought Caryl, and mentioned this to Brad over lunch half an hour later.

'He's a good man, very conscientious. He'd blame himself if he allowed you to stay longer and then Uncle was unwell.'

Brad drove her to the railway station later and waited until the train drew out before leaving. Caryl, relaxing in her first-class compartment, went over the details of her short stay at the manor. She could not help thinking that Emma had lost a great deal by breaking the engagement, yet at the same time she felt, as Emma did, that Brad's rather dictatorial personality would very soon have clashed with Emma's. And inevitably she remembered her own feelings for Brad at that time and wondered how she would have fared if Brad had asked her to marry him instead of asking Emma. The way she had felt, there would have been only one answer. She would have married Brad like a shot without a care for the future and what it might bring in the way of disillusionments.

She was glad he had not asked her, because the 'love' she had had for him would have died by now, seeing that it was only the immature imaginings of a young girl dazzled by the sheer magnificence of the man.

Emma was at the station with the car when the train got into Chester station, and no sooner was Caryl seated beside her than she wanted a full report of all that had transpired. Emma was sad on hearing of Sir Geoffrey's condition, but, like Brad, she felt he had been fortunate in having had a good, healthy life, and a long one.

'So he was really upset by what happened six years ago?'

'He was, Emma. He wondered why I—you weren't married. I felt as if he were hoping, even at this stage, that you and Brad would get together. He certainly thought the world of you.'

'I know, and I felt terrible at disappointing him.'

'You'd have had a good life.'

'But not a happy one. Money isn't everything, Caryl.'

Caryl agreed, and when Emma said she had made up her mind to go out to Patrick, she knew that her sister was doing the right thing.

'When are you thinking of going?' she asked later as

they sat over the light supper Emma had prepared before setting out for the station.

'As soon as possible after you leave. I'm so glad you got the job at Goudham Kennels and can take Sandy. However, you'll have to be on your guard, Caryl. It would be awful if Sir Geoffrey were ever to find out he'd been deceived.'

'Brad assured me that there's no possible chance of his uncle's knowing I'm working on the estate.'

'This man Robert—he'll have to be taken into Brad's confidence, obviously.'

'Of course, but he can be trusted, as you have gathered from what I've been saying about him.'

'And there's no one else who might inadvertently give the game away?'

Caryl shook her head confidently. 'Robert's the only one who looks after Sir Geoffrey. None of the servants go into his rooms, other than to clean, of course, and I expect Robert is always about. In any case, the servants wouldn't be talking to Sir Geoffrey. No, I can't see any risk at all.'

'If you're perfectly satisfied, then, that's fine.'

'You sound troubled.'

'Not really, but I do feel that care is needed.'

'I'll be living at the dower house, so I'm not envisaging being anywhere near the actual manor house.'

'So I was right in thinking that Brad's not married.' Emma changed the subject abruptly. 'He's thirty-two now, so he ought to be looking around.'

'He might have a girl friend, for all we know.'

'But you said he dines alone every night.'

'Which doesn't prove anything,' returned Caryl logically. Suddenly she was recalling that strange look on Louisa's face when Brad had brought her along to show her her bedroom. Why this should come to mind just now Caryl was at a loss to understand for there seemed no reason why it should.

The meal finished, Emma and Caryl both agreed to leave the supper table as it was and go to bed.

'I expect you'll just flake out the moment you touch the pillow,' said Emma understandingly as she watched her sister lift a hand to smother a yawn. 'Sleep well, love—and I'm thrilled that you've managed to get yourself fixed up in a job where Sandy can be with you.'

Caryl was so deeply touched by Miss Haldene's letter of gratitude that tears gathered in her eyes. The elderly invalid lady had expressed thanks over and over again for Caryl's action in saving her dog from being moved to a place where, separated from Caryl, he would surely have died of a broken heart.

It was Friday, and Caryl had been settled in her comfortable little flat for just over a week. She had initially telephoned Miss Haldene outlining the situation and had asked if she would be agreeable for Sandy to be moved to the kennels at Goudham where she, Caryl, would be working. Miss Haldene had agreed at once, and now this letter had arrived—a grateful acknowledgement of what she termed a debt she could never repay.

Slowly Caryl folded the letter and laid it aside. Breakfast was always a hurried meal, and soon she was stepping out into the sunshine, on her way to the kennel block where Sandy was housed. She was met by Avice, one of the maids, who wasted no time in telling her that Sandy was not well.

'What's wrong with him?' Caryl had gone pale, her thoughts quite naturally flying to Miss Haldene and the letter which had arrived from her this morning. 'Have you phoned for the vet?'

'I'm just about to.'

'I'll go and see him,' said Caryl hastily. 'Tell Dr. Keswick it's urgent; he must come over right away.'

'I will,' promised Avice, and sped away in one direction while Caryl ran in another. Sandy was lying in his basket, scarcely breathing, it seemed to Caryl, and her heart gave a great lurch as fear spread over her.

'Sandy . . .' Gently she took him in her arms, pressing his head against her breast. 'You poor little thing. What's happened to you? You were doing so well. . . .' Her voice trailed to silence as she became aware of a shadow falling across the concrete of the cage. Her eyes were misted as she looked up into Brad's dark, enigmatical gaze.

'What's the matter? I saw Avice running to the office; she said she was phoning for the vet, as Sandy was ill.'

'I don't know what's wrong with him—' Suddenly the tears came, falling into Sandy's soft coat. 'If he should die it would be awful for Miss Haldene. I had a letter from her this morning to say how grateful she is—'

'Give him to me,' ordered Brad practically. 'Come, little chap, and let's see what's wrong with you.' With expert hands he examined the dog, pulling gently at his bottom lids, probing his fur to find out if he would cry out to reveal pain. 'I can't find anything. Perhaps it's something he's eaten?'

Caryl shook her head. 'Nothing which is different from his normal diet. I feed him myself, so I know.'

'And of course no one other than you and the other girls have access to the kennels.' He was thoughtful, and Caryl frowned at the idea that he was almost convinced that Sandy had eaten something that had disagreed with him.

'No, no one has access to the kennels—' She stopped abruptly, and Brad shot her a sharp, inquiring glance.

'Yes?' he said tersely, the dog still in his arms.

'It's nothing.' Caryl shook her head, but she was frowning in thought.

'Someone came to see their dog yesterday?'

'No, we didn't have any visitors—well, none who had a dog here.'

'But someone— Caryl, come on out with it,' he commanded. 'If one of you girls has been neglectful, then admit it!'

Caryl hesitated, thinking of the arrogant girl who had sauntered over to the kennels yesterday, the girl who had been over twice before. Marcia Boyle, Brad's girl friend. Supercilious and haughty for no reason at all, she had riled Caryl by asking questions as to how she had obtained a job when, she asserted, there was no vacancy.

'Mr. Craven's never employed more than two girls here. The size of these kennels doesn't warrant the employment of a third kennel-maid!'

'I suggest,' Caryl had said stiffly, 'that you talk to Mr. Craven about it.' At that time she had wondered who the girl was. Avice had soon enlightened her.

'The boss's girl friend. In fact, they're almost engaged. We're expecting the announcement any day. She was asking me about you—seemed exceptionally curious. I said I didn't know anything except that you'd brought Sandy.' Avice paused a moment. She was never very talkative, but her manner now was that of someone who felt it incumbent on her to complete what she had started. 'Marcia kept on asking questions, especially about Sandy's plight, and as she's going to be my employer's wife, I couldn't altogether snub her, but for all that I didn't tell her much—' Avice broke off and grimaced. 'I don't know very much, do I? Not that I want to, because I'm not the curious kind. I mind my own business and don't have the time to bother about anyone else's. However, I eventually told her all I knew about Sandy, and that he was the sole reason you came here. Then she said a very strange thing: she said that if Sandy died, then there'd be nothing for Mr. Craven to keep you on for. She said it so softly that I scarcely heard. It was as if she were speaking to herself.'

'That certainly was a strange thing to say,' Caryl had agreed, little knowing what was in Marcia's mind.

But she knew now! There was little doubt in her mind as she looked at Sandy, lying there in Brad's arms, not a whimper, not a movement in his body. How could Brad even think of marrying such a woman? It was inconceivable! Yet on the surface the girl was beautiful, with her vivid blue eyes and flawless skin, her full red mouth, her svelte figure that sent her glorious hair flying when she moved it in that particular way . . . all these compounded to create the kind of female who would attract any man who happened to set eyes on her.

And Brad was contemplating marriage to her. . . .

'Caryl, I have asked you a question!' His firm, commanding voice recalled her with a start, and she heard herself say, slowly and reluctantly, 'Miss Boyle was here yesterday afternoon—' She paused, then felt obliged to add, even though she lacked sincerity, 'But she wouldn't give Sandy anything.'

'Certainly not. I'm surprised that she should come over, though,' he added with frowning puzzlement. 'What did she want?'

'She just strolled about, looking at the dogs.'

'Is that all?' Brad was still frowning, and suddenly Caryl felt the urge to say, 'She was interested in my being here. She seemed to think there wasn't enough work for three kennel-maids.'

Did his mouth tighten? wondered Caryl. If so it was a fleeting gesture which was certainly not in evidence now.

'She doesn't often come over here to the kennels. . . .' He seemed to be speaking to himself, and Caryl gained the impression that Marcia did not like dogs.

'Avice was saying that Miss Boyle only lives just along the road, in the imposing white house called Haddon Grange.' Why she mentioned this Caryl could not have said. Brad looked at her, passed Sandy into her hands, then strode away through the grounds of the dower house towards the large field where several men were making hay, using all the most up-to-date machinery.

The vet arrived within twenty minutes and stated emphatically that Sandy had eaten something that had disagreed with him. He looked stern, because such things did not normally happen in any well-run kennels.

'I gave him only what I know agrees with him,' said Caryl defensively. 'Is he going to be all right?'

'I'll leave you some medicine and tablets. See that this doesn't occur again!'

'Well,' said Avice when he had gone, 'how did that happen? You're so careful with Sandy. He's the most coddled dog in the kennels!'

'As far as I know, he's had nothing different,' was all Caryl offered, but she had made up her mind to watch Marcia very carefully the next time she came over to the kennels.

That evening she took a stroll in the grounds of the dower house, then found herself walking along a field path which climbed gently, so that from the top of the rise the whole sweeping bay at Bridport was visible. It was late evening and the sun was descending behind the shadowed hills, flooding the sky with crimson and gold which were brilliantly reflected on the mirror-smooth sea, so that it appeared to be on fire. The wonder of it kept Caryl spellbound; she could not move, nor did she want to do so. And then she was aware of feathery ripples along her spine and swept around quickly. Relief brought a sigh to her lips, followed by a smile.

'Robert!' she exclaimed. 'You half frightened me. It's lonely here.'

'Sorry. I should have whistled or coughed or something.' He was beside her, tall and smart and nice to be with. Caryl had seen him a couple of times during the week she had been here, for he would take a stroll over to the kennels during the hour when his charge was sleeping after he had had his lunch. A quiet sort of friendliness had sprung up between them from the moment they had bumped into one another when she had come from one of the cages and seen him standing by the one next to it. He was interested in Sandy, even more interested in the story of Emma and Brad. He obviously felt honoured at being let into the secret and promised to make sure that Sir Geoffrey never had any inkling that he had been deceived. He agreed with Brad that it was impossible for the old man ever to find out that Caryl was working at the kennels.

'I've been watching the sunset—' Caryl made a comprehensive gesture, taking in sea and sky and the purple-sided hills. 'It's wonderful!'

'You've not lived by the sea before?'

She shook her head. 'No, but I think I always will from now on.' She told him about Emma, and the sailing she was looking forward to. 'Have you ever had a boat?' she asked, her eyes wandering back to the harbour and the numerous craft bobbing about in the golden sunset.

'No, but I'd like to have one someday.'

Caryl looked up into his face, saw the rather dreamy expression in his eyes. He seemed lost in thoughts not meant for revealing; Caryl wondered if there had been a tragedy in his life.

'Are you out walking, Robert?' She knew it was his evening off and so was able to add, 'Shall we stroll down to the harbour and have a bite to eat at one of the cafés there?'

'That would be nice,' he readily agreed. 'I feel like company tonight.' Low the voice and faintly sad. Caryl wanted to ask questions but did not quite know what the questions were.

They walked in companionable silence, and when the road leading down to the harbour became rocky, he took her hand in a protective way. It was his instinct to care for people, she realised, and her heart warmed to him.

The café was situated right at the eastern end of the waterfront. It was select and cosy, a little more expensive than the cafés in the more congested part and therefore it was not overcrowded. Candles flickered on the tables, which were tucked away behind tall-growing palms and other potted plants. On each table a rose in all its isolated beauty stood upright in a crystal holder which matched the luminous crystal wineglasses. Caryl and Robert were shown to a table in a corner, where they had a view of the sea. The menu was brought, and they ordered. Caryl had a martini as an aperitif, and Robert had half a pint of beer.

Right out of the blue he said, his eyes broodingly fixed on the froth topping his beer, 'I was feeling very low up there, Caryl, and it seemed like a miracle when you suggested we come here and have a meal. You see, it happens to be an anniversary . . . the anniversary of the death of my fiancée.' He lifted his eyes and saw that Caryl had closed hers under the pain she felt at his words.

'Oh . . . I'm so sorry.' Her voice caught; she wanted to say more, but what was there to say? In any case, a lump had settled in her throat and she was having difficulty removing it.

'It was a car accident. She was a passenger. She'd been offered a lift home and, as she was meeting me that evening, she accepted, even though she had told me the man was a bad driver. They were both killed instantly. She was a nurse. We were planning to marry just before Christmas. . . .' His voice trailed to silence after the succession of relatively short sentences had revealed so much. 'It was a year ago tonight,' he added finally and lifted his glass.

'How—how old was she?' Caryl managed at last.

'Twenty-one,' he said, and again Caryl closed her eyes.

'You must have been devastated.'

He nodded slowly and stared into his glass again. 'I thought I'd never get over it—' He broke off, and a sad smile appeared for a moment. 'I haven't got over it, of course; it takes a long, long time. But at least the excruciating pain is lessening with every day that passes. I left the hospital where I worked in administration—it was the hospital where Mary had worked—because I felt so restless I couldn't do my job properly. Then this post was advertised, and it seemed to be what I needed. It takes up all my waking hours, so my mind's taken off my loss, to some extent.' He stopped, and she saw the hint of apology in his glance. 'I ought not to be telling you my troubles, Caryl. Forgive me—'

'It's good to unburden yourself,' she broke in to assure him. 'Especially tonight you need company and you need to be free to talk. And who else should you talk of than the girl you loved?'

He stared at her, shaking his head as if he were a trifle dazed. 'You're a wonderful person, Caryl,' he said at last. 'I have never met anyone as understanding as you.'

She picked up her martini and took a sip. 'I'm just an ordinary person, Robert. Anyone would be a sympathetic listener in a situation like this.'

Again he shook his head, but this time it was a negative gesture, and when he spoke his tone was bitter. 'My mother and sister both told me to snap out of it. Lots of people suffered tragedies, and if they all went under, where would we be?'

Caryl frowned at such callousness but made no comment. 'You didn't go under' was all she said.

'I almost did, Caryl. I—I tried to commit suicide.'

'But you were strong in the end.' Her smile was almost tender. 'You will get over it, Robert, because time is the infallible healer. But, meanwhile, give your thoughts to Mary, and talk about her just as much as you like.'

'Thank you, Caryl,' he returned simply, but for a while he did not talk at all, simply sat there lost in memories. Caryl listened to the music and enjoyed her food. She was ready to listen when at last Robert broke the long silence to tell her about the girl he had loved. During the conversation later she learned to her surprise that he was twenty-nine years of age. She would have guessed his age at no more than twenty-five at the most.

They walked home in the moonlight, with the sky a deep purple canopy studded with a myriad of diamond sequins. The sea was indigo below the mysterious shades which formed the hills, the stony shoreline an argent sweep of vague, unfathomable contours—the product of nature in its most mysterious workings over eons of time before man even trod the earth. And the silence around them was so complete that Caryl felt urged to break it.

'What a wonderful night, Robert. I know you are feeling sad, but don't you sometimes feel that the beauties of nature are a compensation, however small?'

Robert turned his head to glance down at her. 'You're an exceptional girl' was all he said, and as Caryl made no comment, another silence fell until they reached the front entrance to the dower house. 'Good night, Caryl,' he said, and before she realised what he intended she felt his cool lips pressed against her cheek.

'Good night, Robert.' Her voice was not quite steady, and in her eyes there shone the brightness of unshed tears.

Once in her sitting room the silence of tragedy seemed to close around her, and she moved instinctively to the window and drew aside the drapes. The hills and fields were sleeping, but the sea was moving now, and she stood a long while watching the continuous changing of its face as wispy cirrus clouds swirled across the moon, then floated away again. A deep sadness was holding her spirits down; she knew she would not sleep and decided to go out again, into the breeze and the scents of the gardens surrounding the dower house.

'Caryl!' She stiffened, then relaxed. She had walked much farther than she intended, and it startled her to know she was in the grounds of the manor.

'Brad . . . I'm sorry. I didn't intend to come this far.' She spoke swiftly to hide her embarrassment. 'Sorry,' she said again and would have turned, but to her surprise Brad caught her by the arm and turned her towards him.

'What on earth are you doing wandering about in the dark?' he demanded. 'Nine times out of ten it might be safe, but we do have suspicious characters lurking about at times, just like anyplace else!' He was angry, but it was his imperiousness to which Caryl took exception, his air of mastery, his admonishing attitude.

'I didn't intend to come this far. I've already told you that.'

His eyes glinted at her tone, and her nerves seemed to go tight. For there was an arrogance about him, and a reserve bordering on austerity, which made her feel she had to treat him with deference. And after all, he *was* her employer. She had almost forgotten!

'But you did come this far,' he snapped. 'Don't do it again—at least, not at this time of night. I'll see you back to the dower house.'

He let go of her arm, and to her surprise she missed the warmth, the strength, and even the slight pain which his grip had inflicted.

'Sandy is improving.' She just had to speak, and nothing else came to mind. 'I wonder how it happened.' She was being specious, because she was almost sure that Marcia had a hand in it. 'The vet was angry, which was only to be expected.'

'You must have overfed the dog.'

'I gave him his usual ration.'

'I feel you'll have to be extremely careful with him,' mused Brad. 'Although he's got to know you and you're a comfort to him, he's still fretting for his mistress, and this could affect his whole nervous system, and, in turn, his stomach.'

'I'll be careful,' returned Caryl grimly, her thoughts flying to Marcia. 'Yes, I shall be very careful.'

'I wonder if you'd care to come up for dinner on Thursday.' The invitation was so unexpected that Caryl actually gave a little start of surprise. 'I'm having a small dinner party and would like to invite Robert, just to give him a break. I require a lady to match up the number.'

Marcia would be there, decided Caryl, and she was about to refuse when she thought of Robert. If she turned down Brad's invitation, then Brad might not invite him.

'Thank you,' she returned soberly, 'I'd love to come.'

'I shall expect you about half past seven. We shall dine at eight or just after.' So formal now, just as if they had never known one another in the past, just as if he had never been engaged to her sister . . . just as if he had completely erased from his mind the fact that she had once had a crush on him.

At the door he watched her insert the key and turn it before he bade her good night, then strode away into the moonlit gardens through which he must pass in order to enter the grounds of the manor proper. He was taking a different path from the one she had used a few minutes ago, a path which led to a dark, wooded section of the grounds. Caryl thought she would explore it one day, but not in the dark!

Chapter Four

The ankle-length dress Caryl chose for the dinner party was a delightful creation of sapphire nylon, tight-fitting at the top and full-flowing from the waist down. The cut enhanced the slender lines of her figure, while the colour brought out the blue in her eyes. Her russet-brown hair shone, highlighted with gold; the pearls at her throat lent the final touch of elegance to create perfection.

She had no wrap, so she put a lightweight coat over her shoulders, picked up her small blue satin evening bag, and went out into the warm evening air of the gardens. As she swung out of the drive something made her turn; Avice was at her window upstairs, and the two girls lifted a hand to each other. Avice must be puzzled as to where she was going, thought Caryl and hoped she would not ask any questions tomorrow morning when they met at the kennels.

Lights flared above the house as Caryl approached. Three cars were on the forecourt, none of which was Brad's. She suddenly felt apprehensive, then remembered that she had already dined once at the manor, so all was not to be new to her. She wondered about the guests, though, yet she need not have worried, because she managed to fit in very well—except that Marcia was cool to the point of hostility, her glance critical, her mouth sneering as she said, making sure no one heard except Caryl, 'And how do you come to be here? There's some mystery about you, Miss Chapman, and I'd very much like to know what it is.'

'I did advise you to ask Mr. Craven about me,' Caryl coolly reminded her. 'Obviously you haven't done so.'

The older girl's eyes glinted, but she made no comment on what Caryl had said. She had come up to Caryl, leaving the couple with whom she had been chatting. Caryl, watching her approach, could not but admire the assurance with which she moved across the floor, the sway of the slender hips, the way the girl held her sherry glass, the smile she gave to someone in passing. Clad in silver lamé evening pants and jacket, her hair gleaming as if in competition with the diamonds at her throat, she quite easily succeeded in turning every head, and to Caryl she was to all outward appearances the perfect wife for a man like Brad. All charm when speaking to him, she found no difficulty in concealing her true nature. Why were men so blind? The veneer was all that drew them; they fell for superficial beauty and recklessly chose not to probe beneath the surface. Really, it served them right if, later, they met with disillusionment! Caryl grimaced at her musings as she waited for the girl to reach her. She had known instinctively that whatever Marcia had to say would be unpleasant.

She watched her now as she sipped her sherry, and then, as if sensing Caryl's discomfiture, Robert came up and Marcia instantly moved away.

'She doesn't like me,' he commented in a casual tone. 'And from what I noticed she doesn't like you either.'

'Why is she like that? She doesn't even know me.' For a moment Caryl thought of telling Robert about her suspicions regarding Sandy's indisposition but decided against it. After all, she had no proof that Marcia had been responsible for it.

'Marcia's jealous of any young woman who has any sort of contact with Mr. Craven.' Robert's eyes were following her as she crossed the drawing room to join a couple chatting over by the window. They had been introduced to Caryl by Brad, who explained that they had recently bought a rope-making factory in Bridport and Brad did a small amount of business with them. 'She seems always to be very confident of her hold on him,' Robert was saying, 'and yet she can't stand any other young woman to come anywhere near him.'

Marcia and the couple had been joined by Joan and Philip Wright, who lived in a delightful old-world cottage about four miles from the manor. They had come there a couple of years ago to retire, but Philip found he could not be idle and had now begun growing orchids in a big way.

Brad came over to join Caryl and Robert. 'It's a great pity that Uncle can't be here,' he said. 'He used to enjoy having guests to dinner.'

'If it wasn't for his sight he'd be able to come. We'd be able to get him this far without too much trouble.'

Brad nodded in agreement. 'As you say, it's his sight.'

'And nothing can be done about it.'

The two men continued to talk about Sir Geoffrey, and Caryl found herself studying Brad intently. She thought of what Avice had said about the expected announcement of his engagement to Marcia and wondered if he was really in love with the girl or whether it was a kind of marriage of suitability as often occurs within the circle of the aristocracy. She felt sure that Marcia's family were wealthy and asked Robert when, later, she found herself sitting next to him at the dinner table.

'Yes, her family's wealthy,' he said. 'But Marcia's wealthy in her own right. She inherited around a million from an aunt who idolised her.' His eyes followed the line of Caryl's gaze, and he shook his head in a kind of puzzled gesture. 'I can't think what he sees in her—except the surface beauty, of course. I'll not deny that she's just about the most beautiful woman I have ever met.'

'I suppose she hides her real self from him.'

'Undoubtedly she does. She's charming with him at all times. Yet I somehow get the impression that, behind his back, she's laughing at him.'

'Laughing?' Caryl couldn't imagine anyone laughing at a man like Brad. And she fell to wondering what his reaction would be were he to discover he was being laughed at.

'I'd even go as far as to say she's capable of ridiculing him.'

'But no one could ridicule Brad!'

'Be careful,' he warned. 'You're not supposed to call him Brad.'

'I realised my slip immediately I'd made it. Do you suppose she heard?'

'Don't know. She's a small distance away, but she's all ears. You can tell by her lack of concentration on the talk going on close to her. Her eyes repeatedly seek out you and me.'

'To get back to what we were saying about her ridiculing Brad. I just can't imagine why she should.'

'I did say it was only an idea—or at least I implied it. Yet I still believe she's capable of such conduct.'

'Where her own fiancé's concerned? Surely she's aware of the loyalty she owes him.'

'She'd not care about loyalty. And she's not yet engaged to him. I wondered at first if this party was being given to mark the event, and I suppose Mr. Craven could still make the announcement—'

'You do?' Something strange and indefinable caught at Caryl's nerve ends. 'Tonight—now?' What was the matter with her? Why had Robert's words set in motion a disturbance which was affecting her whole nervous system?

'Not exactly now, but later. However, it doesn't concern us whether it's tonight or some other time. She'll have him, that's for sure.'

Caryl fell silent, actually brooding over what Robert had been saying. She was unhappy and yet knew it was illogical, since what Brad did had nothing whatsoever to do with her. He would act as he chose, and if it was his intention and his wish to make Marcia his wife, then he would do just that. But Caryl supposed that at this stage in her musings the fact of her own past feelings for Brad should leap to the forefront of her mind. And her eyes wandered to his face, handsome and noble in the amber light from candles flickering in their silver-gilt sconces. She sensed the degree of mastery in his manner, was vitally conscious of his remarkable bearing, distinguished and austere. Dangerously masculine, she thought, even though there seemed to be a certain coldness about him tonight that matched the cool superiority of the woman who, according to Robert, was confident of her hold on him.

Suddenly he became aware of Caryl's concentrated stare, and their eyes met and held for a long moment before Caryl dropped hers, a wave of colour staining her cheeks because she felt as if she had been caught in some guilty act. Robert spoke, and the tenseness fell away; she smiled and answered him, alive to Marcia's steady gaze and her puzzlement.

When dinner was over the guests drank coffee in the drawing room; then some of them stood around again, socialising. Caryl was talking to Robert when Brad detached himself from the couple he was talking to and came over to join them. Someone spoke to Robert, asking about Sir Geoffrey, and he moved away, leaving Caryl with Brad. To her surprise Caryl heard Brad say, 'I didn't tell you how charming you look tonight. This colour suits you, and the style of the dress is perfect.' A sweep of his eyes over her figure accompanied the words; then his gaze was fixed on her face.

She willed herself not to blush and managed a cool and casual 'Thank you, Brad,' which for some obscure reason brought a quirk of amusement to his mouth. Caryl, instantly remembering Robert's warning, said half apologetically, 'I ought not to be calling you Brad, ought I?'

He frowned down at her and said, 'Why not? It's my name.'

'As your employee I should be calling you Mr. Craven.'

At that he laughed. Caryl looked at him and remembered how, in the old days, when he laughed like that her heart seemed to turn right over.

'I'm quite sure there is no necessity for that, Caryl,' he said. 'After all, I almost became your brother-in-law, didn't I?'

She nodded, her eyes on the wine in her glass. 'Your uncle spoke of the broken engagement and wondered why neither of you had married before now.' She spoke quietly, aware of being watched intently by the tall, slim girl with the cold gleam of hostility in her eyes.

'He never really got over it.' Brad's voice was also low, and without expression. 'It just wasn't to be,' he added, and his dark, metallic eyes wandered in the same direction as his companion's.

She said without looking at him, 'You'll marry one day, of course—with owning all this. A man wants an heir—usually.'

'I don't own all this,' he corrected.

'One day you will.' There was a curious dryness in her throat which lent a high-pitched note to her voice as she added, 'Marriage is a must for a man in your position.'

'You seem extraordinarily concerned about my future.' His tone was dry and faintly cynical.

'I didn't mean to convey that impression.'

'What impression did you mean to convey?' His eyes mocked her, bringing back memories.

'I suppose I was merely trying to make polite conversation,' she said, forcing a smile. 'Perhaps we should change the subject.' She realised she was endeavouring to keep him with her, just as she used to do in the old days.

'I agree.' Brad took a drink and then asked her if she was enjoying the party.

'Very much,' she responded eagerly. 'It's wonderful! Thank you for inviting me.'

'Thank you for coming. I needed you.' His eyes wandered again, to where Marcia was chatting to three men. Caryl saw her murmur something as a lull occurred, and then she disappeared through the door which was opened for her by James. She seemed to be away a long time, and Caryl decided she must have gone to the cloakroom—or perhaps one of the bedrooms—to repair her makeup. There was certainly a heady waft of perfume when she returned. Her eyes immediately sought Caryl's, and there was an expression in them that could only be described as malevolent. Caryl stared and shook her head, an instinctive gesture, as if she would ward off something evil. Then Marcia turned away to talk to a Mr. and Mrs. Holdsworth, who owned two hotels in Lyme Regis, and Caryl began to wonder if she had imagined that expression on the girl's face.

Robert came back, and after a moment or two Brad moved away to join the group which now surrounded Marcia.

'I'm off duty tomorrow evening,' Robert said rather hesitantly, 'and I wondered if you'd care to go to the café again for a meal.'

'Of course.' Eagerly and with a swift smile. 'I'd enjoy that, Robert.'

'Good. I'll call for you if you like—or perhaps you'd rather not have me come to your flat?'

'I don't mind. Come at about half past seven.'

He seemed happy at her quick acceptance, and she realised why he had seemed hesitant: he was doubtful whether or not she would want to go out with him after the sad confidences of last time.

How very nice he was. Caryl hoped that one day he would recover from his loss and find someone he could love as much as he had loved Mary.

The following morning Caryl was much relieved to find Sandy very greatly improved, and she laughed when he wagged his short little tail. She fed him, then stiffened as she saw Marcia coming towards her across the field. She was early, thought Caryl with a sudden frown, because it struck her that there was an air of urgency about the girl. Caryl left the cage, slipping the bolt into place. It was Avice who had let Marcia into the outer passage the last time, and Caryl was going to make sure Marcia didn't enter it this time. She turned to face the girl, aware of the starkly apparent difference in their appearances. Marcia was in well-pressed slacks and a white, short-sleeved blouse, while Caryl was dressed for the job she had to perform, her denims spattered with mud and her blouse bearing the paw marks of Sandy and another dog which persistently would put his paws on her shoulders when she went in to clean his cage. He was a German shepherd dog of exceptional size.

'Did you want something?' Caryl asked, assuming a rather haughty pose to match that of the other girl.

'I'd like a word with you in private!'

'You would?' Caryl flicked a glance around her. 'We're private here, Miss Boyle,' she began when Marcia rudely interrupted her.

'One of the others is likely to come along. We'll go into the office and make sure we're not disturbed.'

'I'm afraid I am exceedingly busy,' said Caryl in crisp tones. 'If the matter isn't urgent, then—'

'I've a few things to ask you, Miss Chapman—now!'

Caryl shrugged and followed the girl to the wooden building that served as an office. She was reluctant to leave her work but yet curious to know what this was all about.

Once in the office with the door closed, Marcia wasted no time in saying, a glitter of venom in her eyes, 'You dined alone with Brad—with Mr. Craven the first day you were here. Why?'

Caryl's eyes opened to their fullest extent. 'Why?' she repeated as if she had not heard aright. 'What has it to do with you, I should like to know?'

'A great deal! I'm engaged to your employer, and as his fiancée I've a right to know just why you were dining alone with him—*and why you slept at the manor!*'

Caryl stared in disbelief at the girl's total lack of tact. 'How do you know I dined with Brad and stayed at his home?' she demanded, that firm little chin uplifted in a gesture which Mrs. Blakeman would have recognised.

'That,' Marcia almost spat out, 'is my business!'

'And mine,' retorted Caryl swiftly. 'We're talking about me, remember. Who told you I'd slept at the manor?'

'I have no intention of telling you! All I want to know is how such a situation came about.'

A small silence followed as Caryl pondered. She was seeing Marcia leave the room last evening. She had been gone a long time and on her return she had cast that vicious look at Caryl. . . . Did it mean that Marcia had talked to someone while she had been out of the room? If so, then who was it? A puzzle which Caryl knew would not be solved at this present time.

'I have no intention of telling you how it came about,' returned Caryl, using some of Marcia's own words. 'Your conduct, incidentally, is disgusting. Do you often forget the demands of delicacy and refinement?'

'Why, you—!' Marcia's teeth snapped together; her eyes blazed with the fury of ignited passion. 'How dare you speak to me like that? I shall have you dismissed—without notice!'

'I think not,' argued Caryl with a calmness she did not altogether feel. The girl's unbridled fury was filling the very air with tension. 'You, Miss Boyle, do not happen to be my employer. I am very sure that Brad will not dismiss me. However, if you feel—'

'Brad! You use his name as freely as if you were his—his—'

'Be careful,' warned Caryl gently. 'If you continue to insult me, I shall retaliate by making a complaint to my employer. You're insulting him as well, aren't you? He's not going to take kindly to that.'

Marcia's whole body quivered with the tumult within her. Caryl thought about Robert's assertion that she felt confident of her hold on Brad, but if that were true, then there would be no need for behaviour like this.

'I shall find out why you slept at the manor!' The girl's voice still vibrated, but it had lost a little of its grating quality.

'Brad's the one to ask,' returned Caryl, fully aware she was goading the girl. 'As your fiancé, I feel sure he'll want to set your mind at rest.'

Marcia glowered at her, gritting her teeth. She tried

to speak but either found it too difficult or changed her mind. She wrenched at the door, flounced through it, and slammed it behind her.

Moving slowly to the window, Caryl reached it in time to see her striding swiftly towards the kennel block where Sandy was housed, fury in every step she took. Caryl watched intently as the girl slowed her pace and then stopped to look in at the little dog. Marcia turned her head, looking towards the office, then strode on again and was eventually lost to sight behind the elegant edifice of the dower house.

Why had she stopped to look at Sandy? Had she expected to find him ill, or perhaps dead? Was it really possible that she had deliberately meant to cause an innocent animal harm just so she could get rid of Caryl? Robert had maintained that Marcia was jealous of any female who came into contact with Brad—if that female was attractive, that was. In short, Marcia feared competition—in spite of the fact that she was supposed to be one hundred percent confident of holding Brad. Well, it was plain that she was not fully confident, for otherwise she would not be the least interested in Caryl or curious as to the relationship existing between her and Brad. Caryl wondered if Marcia now realised the unlikelihood of her bringing about her dismissal. She must know that there was a little more between her and Brad than the cold and practical situation of employer and employee.

Caryl was ready and waiting when Robert came for her, and they had an enjoyable meal, as before. Robert talked a little about Mary, and yet he was not so sad as he had been on that previous occasion. But then that had been the anniversary of his fiancée's death. Caryl talked about herself, and Robert interjected with the information that Sir Geoffrey seemed to be brooding a great deal and never a day went by without his mentioning 'Emma's' recent visit. It was plain, Robert said, that he would still like to see her married to his nephew.

Caryl frowned, and a few seconds elapsed before she spoke. 'It's obvious that Sir Geoffrey isn't happy about Marcia.'

'He doesn't know just how serious it is. But in any case, Marcia's absolutely charming with him—to his face, that is,' he added with a sort of grim recollection which made him knit his brows.

It also spurred Caryl to ask without thinking, 'And behind his back—what's she like then?'

'She positively sneers on the very rare occasions she speaks to me about him. She actually said it was time he made everything over to his nephew, because he was just an automaton now, without either the interest or the ability to own such a vast estate.'

'Oh—how could she be so cruel?'

Robert shrugged. 'You and I know she's not a nice person, Caryl. You've seen what she's like, and so have I.'

'She knew I'd stayed at the manor,' Caryl told him after a slight hesitation. 'I can't think how she found out, but somehow I feel convinced it was when she went from the room last night—perhaps you remember her being gone for some time?'

Robert nodded thoughtfully. 'Louisa used to work at Marcia's home,' he responded, a frown on his brow. 'When Mr. Boyle died, his wife closed up some of the rooms and Louisa became redundant. She was taken on by Mr. Craven. . . .' Robert's voice trailed and Caryl knew what he was thinking even before he made the suggestion that Louisa might have chatted to Marcia and mentioned the fact that Caryl had stayed at the manor. 'She was very devoted to Marcia, from what I have heard,' Robert went on, 'and she'll be very happy when Marcia comes to live at the manor. Perhaps Louisa was a bit troubled on discovering that her employer was friendly with a pretty girl like you—'

'Louisa did look at me rather strangely,' broke in Caryl with haste. 'And after she had shown me to my room I had the impression that she would have liked to ask me questions, but of course she refrained.' It was all falling into place, and Caryl had no doubts now about where Marcia had gained her knowledge.

'And did Marcia actually tell you she knew you'd stayed? It's only just struck me that she must have done.' His eyes questioned, and he was suddenly shaking his head in disbelief.

'She wanted to know why I had stayed the night, said she had a right to know.'

Robert's brows lifted. 'What impudence! She must feel very confident of marrying Mr. Craven. It would serve her right if he threw her over.'

'She said she and he were engaged to be married.'

'Well, it's never been announced, so I'd say it was wishful thinking on her part.' Robert paused a moment, and then: 'She appears to be extremely bothered about you and your relationship with Mr. Craven.'

'It would seem so. She says she means to find out why I stayed at the manor.'

'And how does she propose to do that?'

'I am afraid I was catty; I told her to ask Brad.'

Robert smiled his approval, but before he could comment Caryl veered the conversation into a different channel because she did not particularly want to talk about that detestable girl anymore. She talked about her sister, telling Robert that she had had a letter from her that morning to say she had definitely made up her mind to join her fiancé in Nigeria and she would be going soon.

'She'll get married there?' he asked interestedly.

'I expect so. I'd have liked to be at the wedding, but it's impossible.'

'It seems unbelievable to me that she should have given up Mr. Craven and the good life she would have had at the manor.'

'She didn't love him, Robert, and, after all, love is the most important thing in marriage, isn't it?'

'It would be for me, but for some people it doesn't take priority. Many women would have seized the opportunity of becoming the wife of a man like Mr. Craven.'

Caryl nodded, thinking again of Marcia, who obviously did not love Brad. On the other hand, she was not interested in his money—or shouldn't be—since she had so much of her own. Caryl rather thought that prestige came into it strongly, Marcia being the kind of woman who would revel in being the lady of the manor. Also, Brad was handsome and distinguished, a man who would inevitably turn every female head in his direction wherever he might be, and so he was the kind of man to whom a woman like Marcia would enjoy being married, since she would always be conscious of the fact that all other women envied her. Caryl wondered how she would feel were she to know that, had Emma not decided to break off her engagement six years ago, then she would never have had the chance of becoming Brad's wife.

Robert stood for a while after taking Caryl to the door of her flat. He had fallen into a quiet reverie on the way up from the restaurant, and Caryl, wondering if he were thinking about Mary, did not attempt to bring him out of it. A year wasn't long; in any case, he needed something else to come into his life in order that his mind could be taken off the tragedy. True, he was occupied with Sir Geoffrey, but there were the evenings after the old man had gone to bed at eight o'clock. From what Caryl could gather Robert just sat in his room and read, or sometimes he would take a short stroll, but never for more than a few minutes, just in case he was needed.

'It's a beautiful night.' Caryl's eyes wandered to the dark profile of the cliffs falling down to a sea spangled with moonglow; then they wandered to the harbour and its myriad twinkling lights, flickering in and out as holidaymakers passed before them as they strolled along the waterfront—carefree, happy people here for a fortnight's vacation, living in the brightly painted caravans or the holiday bungalows which formed a delightful little estate to the east of the bay. 'Just look at those stars! And that bright moon. . . .' Caryl looked up into Robert's face, and a great sadness swept over her at his loss. 'Perhaps—perhaps you don't see the beauty?'

'Yes, I do, Caryl,' he argued gently. 'Oh, yes, I do . . . but it brings back so many memories—' Abruptly he stopped, and she wondered if he were crying but would not look in case she should embarrass him, and so she swung around to stare silently towards the rising dark shape of the manor. It was the back she could see from here, and it seemed faintly formidable. But the front would be brilliantly lighted, and the fountain would throw off a million star spangles as its waters caught the reflection from the lamps along the side of the ornamental pool, a pool where water lilies flourished and goldfish swam about among other aquatic vegetation.

A wonderful house . . . and a wonderful man who owned it. A man far too good for the woman whom he was intending to marry.

'Good night, Robert,' she murmured, coming around again to face him. 'Thank you for a most pleasant evening.'

'We'll do it again on my evening off?'

She smiled and nodded her head. 'Of course we shall.'

'You're helping me, Caryl,' he said simply, and, as before, he kissed her on the cheek. 'Good night, dear, and sleep well.'

Chapter Five

Caryl stared at Brad in disbelief, shaking her head from side to side as if trying to clear her brain so that she could be sure she had heard aright.

'Are you serious?' was all she could produce when at last she did speak.

'Uncle wants it, Caryl. It will make him happy if you and I marry.'

'So you *are* serious—I mean, you've just asked me to marry you, Brad.' She spoke rather more distinctly than was necessary, for she felt she must stress every word, just to make him fully aware of the step he wanted to take.

'He believes you're Emma, of course—or he will do if you agree to marry me,' went on Brad just as if Caryl had not spoken. 'That will have to be kept up, obviously.'

'He's been talking to you?'

'Of course. As a matter of fact, he's been restless ever since you visited him—since Emma visited him. He asked me to propose to her again.'

'It's impossible! We're not in love!'

'Maybe we shall manage it one day,' he returned rather casually, yet with a hint of amusement in his finely timbred voice. 'I shan't make demands on you,' he assured her after a pause, 'so you needn't worry about that.'

The frown on Caryl's brow smoothed out as her mind cleared. She looked straight at him and said, 'Everyone believes you're in love with Miss Boyle—that your engagement is shortly to be announced. Is that correct?' Very blunt the question, but Caryl wanted everything made clear— She cut her thoughts. What was she thinking of? There was no question of her marrying Brad! No, not even for Sir Geoffrey's sake.

'It is correct that we were almost engaged,' he admitted with a frankness that surprised her. 'However, I feel I ought to do as my uncle wishes and marry you—or Emma—' He broke off, and Caryl sensed a slight impatience about him as a result of the mix-up.

She looked at him, suspicion in her steady gaze. Brad was not the man to give up the woman he loved merely for the sake of pandering to the wishes of an old man.

'There's something I don't understand,' she said, sighing with bewilderment. But it was her own feelings that bewildered her the most, for she was fighting against some insistent feeling of acute unrest which had sprung itself upon her and which she was quite unable to shake off. Visions of Marcia married to Brad obscured all other pictures except the one of herself married to him. . . .

'There's nothing complicated about the business,' he

said calmly, lifting a hand to stifle a yawn. 'You haven't a young man, so there isn't anything there to complicate matters. For myself—I wish to make Uncle happy and an willing to marry you in order to do so.'

'But what about the future?' she cried. 'Marriage is for a lifetime, Brad!'

'I agree.' His glance was cool, his voice impersonal. 'I am not suggesting a temporary marriage made for no other reason than to make Uncle Geoffrey happy.'

'There's another reason, then?' Caryl was swift to inquire, and she did wonder if he was taken aback by her question.

If so, he very soon recovered, for the calm lack of emotion was still in his voice when he spoke. 'You apparently misunderstood me, Caryl. What I am saying is that the marriage will be permanent, and although the relationship will be platonic at first, I did say there is a chance of our falling in love with one another.' He looked at her and for a moment said nothing.

She glanced down at her clothes, her thoughts going to that moment when Louisa had come to her as she was feeding one of the dogs. Mr. Craven wished to speak with her, and so would she go at once to the manor? Louisa had seemed faintly hostile but could have had no inkling of what it was her employer wanted to see Caryl about.

'You're a most attractive girl, as I believe I have already said. It is not beyond the bounds of possibility that I should fall in love with you.'

She looked at him swiftly, her nerve ends tingling. The years slid away, dissolved into nothingness as they coalesced with the present, and she was seeing, as if in a vision of absolute, undeniable truth, that she had not changed . . . she still loved him. What she had felt for him all that time ago was no schoolgirl crush, as she had come later to believe; it was love in all its untarnished purity, love deep and strong and timelessly enduring. The world, the elements, the vast and fearful void of eternity . . . all were as nothing beside the love she felt for him in this moment of revelation, a love simple and primordial yet boundless as infinity. It had lain dormant, denied life because of lack of nurture, but it had sprung to life now, awakened by the words Brad had just uttered.

She continued to stare at him—tall and magnificent and excitingly masculine, with those noble features, that wind-burned skin telling of the outdoor life he lived.

He moved as if in impatience, yet on his face was a look of understanding, and she gave a deep sigh and said slowly, 'If—if I thought we would one day fall in love . . .' She tailed off, thinking of Marcia again and his admission that he and she were almost engaged. He had evaded the first part of her question, and she did not want to ask it again, did not want to know whether or not he had been in love with the girl. For surely if he had then this present situation would never have arisen. Unless there was another reason . . . No. Caryl resolutely put all thoughts from her except that she loved Brad with a love as fierce as any pagan woman from the primitive jungle. 'I'll marry you,' she said, and her voice was calm and clear, but quiet, like her clasped hands which gave the impression of total tranquillity. A smile parted her lips. Brad moved close, took her face in his hands, and, bending his head, he kissed her gently and held her a moment, as if to reassure her that she had not made a mistake. Her eyes as they looked into his were limpid, the stars in their depths created by moisture, unshed tears of happiness.

'It'll be a nine-days' wonder,' she was saying a few moments later when Brad, stating they must drink to the success of the marriage, handed her a glass of sparkling champagne.

'Undoubtedly it will. But soon everyone will get used to it.'

Caryl looked into the long, slender glass and watched the bubbles rising . . . like her hopes. But soon faces floated before her mental vision—Marcia, Louisa, Emma, Robert, Avice. . . . What would their reactions really be? Would they get used to it? Robert had obviously hoped she would be a companion to him, going out on his evenings off, helping him over his unhappiness. Emma would ask all sorts of questions and probably call her the world's greatest fool for marrying without love. Emma was always so wise, so farseeing. Caryl hoped she would not meddle too much, or cast down her spirits by saying Caryl would surely come to regret this impulsive decision. Avice . . . she would wonder, but that was all. She had never tried to become friendly with Caryl, and the other kennel-maid worked in the other block and so Caryl scarcely knew her at all. Louisa, who would be upset because her idol had not married Brad. Lastly there was Marcia. . . . Caryl shuddered involuntarily, and the champagne spilled onto her hand. Was it an omen? Silly to be suspicious over nothing! Wine often was spilled.

'What is it, Caryl? You've gone rather pale.'

Brad's anxious inquiry brought a forced smile to her lips. With an effort she replied, 'It's nothing, Brad. . . . Er—what are we drinking to?'

'Happiness,' he answered briefly and leant forward to touch her glass with his.

'Happiness.' She drank, but within her there was an elusive, disturbing emotion which she was unable to define.

'We must tell Uncle the good news as soon as possible,' Brad was saying.

'He doesn't know I am here. Shall you say I am coming down—that you proposed over the phone, or something?'

'I think so.' Brad nodded thoughtfully as he spoke. 'We shall have always to remember that you are Emma. It won't be easy, but we must never let him know he's been deceived.'

'Marcia . . . She won't be coming over in future, will she?'

The anxiety in her voice was bound to come over to him, and he answered gently and with a reassuring smile. 'No, Caryl, she'll not be coming over. Everything is finished between her and me.' Grimness in the voice now, and the eyes were hard as tempered steel. The hand holding the glass seemed to clench, and Caryl waited, eyes wide, for the stem to snap. Brad raised the glass and seemed to relax. 'To our future, Caryl. Let us hope we can make it worthwhile.'

She looked at him, and a frown touched her brow. For it seemed a strange thing to say—as if he had some doubts about their being able to make their future worthwhile.

'If we try,' she faltered, suddenly on the edge of tears—and they would not be tears of happiness this time. 'We have to—to try hard, Brad—every marriage needs effort.'

'Don't worry, Caryl,' he said, and, putting his glass down, he moved towards her. He took her glass, held it a moment as he stared into her eyes, then placed it on a table. 'Come, child, this is not the time for tears and fears. You and I have just become engaged to be married. Off you go to smarten up. I'm taking you out for a celebration dinner.' He smiled, and her tension eased instantly.

They went into Dorchester to the Angel, Brad, handsome and immaculate, driving his Mercedes and Caryl trying to relax in the comfortable seat beside him. She was wearing a pastel blue polka-dotted dress in organza trimmed with Swiss organdie flowers which also embellished the frilled neckline. The skirt was full-flowing from a nipped-in waist above which the tight-fitting bodice hugged her firm young breasts in the most alluring way. Her hair shone because she had shampooed it for the occasion, and as they entered the restaurant her eyes shone, too, because she was happy, her fears and anxieties having all dissolved. Brad had ordered a special table tucked away in an alcove subtly lit by one wall lamp and the flickering light from a branch of candles set on a tall wrought-iron stand at the back of which was an imitation gate also of wrought iron. Trained up its sides and over the top was a decorative ivy, thick and green, its leaves bright and gleaming in the glow from the wall lamp.

'It's very romantic,' Caryl heard herself say, and then she coloured up and was glad that the glow all around was rosy. She felt sure her blush had gone unnoticed but knew her impulsive words had not. Would Brad think her silly, attaching romance to a marriage arranged as cold-bloodedly as theirs had been only a few short hours earlier? She glanced at him from under her lashes, but his face was a mask.

'We must have champagne again,' he said, lifting a finger to bring the wine waiter over to the table. 'You would like that?'

'I love champagne,' she returned enthusiastically.

The meal was a success, with Brad talking about the wedding, and about his uncle, who would want to be there. Robert must be persuaded to bring him.

'It will be a great pleasure for him to be at our wedding. Our marriage has been something he has wanted all this time, even though it was only recently that he asked me to send for Emma to come down to see him.'

'It seems strange to think of myself as Emma.'

'It'll only be when you're with him.'

'I think I shall try to spend a little time with him every day—if Robert will let me, that is.'

'Uncle would like that, Caryl. He hasn't much time left, and it will be rewarding for you to know you made him happy in the last months of his life.'

'Months?' Sadness stole over her, erasing her happiness for a space.

'Six months at the most—unless I am very much mistaken. The doctor hasn't said it in so many words, but he hinted at it a couple of weeks ago.'

'Old age is the saddest thing,' murmured Caryl, wondering what it must feel like to be nearing the end of your life. She'd heard it said you became tired and didn't care very much at all.

It was still sad, though, and a deep sigh escaped her, which made Brad say a little sharply, 'Put it out of your mind for the present, Caryl. This is a celebration.' He paused as the waiter came along to refill the glasses.

'Tomorrow we shall come into Dorchester to choose a ring for you.'

A ring. . . . Only now did the engagement seem real. . . . She had not been dreaming; she was to become Brad's wife . . . the lady of the manor.

They lingered over the meal, so that it was fairly late when Brad stopped the car outside the imposing front entrance to the dower house. He got out and opened the door for Caryl, and they stood a few minutes, talking. For Caryl it was magical because of Brad's attitude towards her. He was kind and understanding and yet at the same time casual in that he seemed anxious for her not to feel any strain or suffer any misgivings. She felt totally optimistic for the future, seeing herself as a well-loved wife and mother, and that was all she wanted from life—contentment and love.

From where they stood the sea was a bright mirror, and Brad remarked on its smoothness. 'Often it is rough,' he added with a grim inflection. 'You'll see the waves lift high in the air and then sweep right onto the road.'

'They reach that far?'

'And bring huge boulders with them. I've often seen the road strewn with debris from the beach.'

Caryl said nothing; she was content to be quiet, content to have Brad with her, and it certainly seemed as if he were in no hurry to leave her just yet. She looked around at the drowsy scene, aware of a sort of sultry fascination about the atmosphere—the moon, motionless and splendid, spilling gold onto the ocean, the trail of stars in glamourous profusion, spangling the purple dome of the heavens, the magical blending of both sea and sky in a haze of dramatic untransparency which made the horizon feel close. The air was scented and heady, the breeze warm and purring against the sepia undulations of the low hills which, like the horizon, seemed close.

'Well,' said Brad at last, 'it is time I was leaving you.' He looked down into her face and smiled. She remembered other times long past when he had smiled like that and her heart had seemed to melt. But his smile had not been for her but for Emma, and for some reason Emma had not been affected by it very much at all.

'Yes—it's late.'

'I suppose you still want to look after Sandy.'

She nodded and said yes, of course she did. 'But you won't like my working at the kennels, I suppose,' she felt bound to add.

'I can't have you working, Caryl,' he said in quiet but very firm and unarguable tones. 'I shan't mind your continuing to come over and care for Sandy, but you'll not be cleaning his kennel out. One of the others will do that.'

'Yes, I understand.' Lady of the manor . . . How would she live up to standards like that? Yet Emma had once contemplated doing so, and as far as Caryl could remember she had found nothing daunting about the idea.

'I'll see you tomorrow and we can make arrangements for the wedding, but first we shall go into Dorchester for the ring. I'll call for you about half past ten or thereabouts.' She watched him slide into the car, stood there until the taillights had disappeared, and then she turned and went slowly indoors.

Caryl chose a solitaire diamond, and Brad put it on her finger a couple of hours later when they had gone into a restaurant to have lunch. It felt and looked strange to her, its flawless brilliance catching the shaft of sunlight streaming through the window by which they were sitting. Brad noticed her moving her finger, and a faint smile touched the firm outline of his mouth. But on the whole there was a detached air about him, and unfathomable shadows made his eyes seem darker than ever. Where were his thoughts at this moment as he looked at the ring on her finger? Marcia? Caryl was relieved when the waitress came up to the table to take the order.

'Aren't the flowers pretty?' She spoke for the sake of it, hoping to divert his mind from she knew not what. 'It's such a pity they die so soon.'

He looked at the three lovely carnations in the white porcelain vase. 'Like us, they have their day,' he said, and it seemed that the words came out on a tiny sigh.

Caryl tried to ignore it as she said, 'A linnet's wing might have touched this.' She was fingering one of the flowers caressingly. 'It's believed that flowers can think. I wish they could speak.'

'A linnet's wing . . .' He seemed not to have heard the rest. 'You're a rather special person,' he said unexpectedly. 'Why aren't you married already?'

She averted her eyes; she now knew why no one else had ever appealed to her, but she merely said in answer to his question, 'The right one didn't come along.' And when he did not speak she lifted her eyes, to catch again that brooding, shadowed look in his gaze. She supposed he was thinking that the right one hadn't really come along now, but how little he knew! No doubt at times he recalled that 'crush' she'd had on him—for she supposed he still regarded it as that—but she did wonder what his reaction would be if she were to confess that it had not been a trivial, transient emotion at all, but the real thing, and what she felt for him now was an extension of her feelings then.

However, confessions were not for the present; they might be for the future, she hoped, and at these musings a smile fluttered unconsciously to her lips.

'You're happy about all this?' he asked, breaking a rather long silence.

'Of course.'

'It's strange what fate does to us.'

'Fate?' Her eyes became soft with appeal. 'Fate had no part in this, Brad,' she asserted gently. 'We both made our decisions of our own free wills—so much so that we could change our minds this very moment if we wanted to.'

Brad knit his brows. 'You'd not do that, would you?' He sounded a trifle anxious, she thought, and her smile deepened to reassure him.

'I have no reason to, have I?'

'Not at present, but you might have later.'

It was Caryl's turn to frown. 'That's a strange thing to say, Brad.' She moved uneasily as a sense of powerlessness swept over her.

It was broken instantly when Brad said, 'Certainly it was, my dear. I'm sure you'll not have cause to change your mind. In any case,' he added, 'we can't delay, because once Uncle knows of our engagement he's going to expect the wedding to take place almost immediately.'

'You'll tell him today?'

Brad nodded thoughtfully. 'We'll go in to him together, I think. I shall say that I phoned you, asking you to marry me. You agreed, much to my surprise, and you wasted no time in coming down to Dorset. You arrived late last evening, and so we didn't want to disturb or excite him at that time.' Brad stopped and shrugged his shoulders. 'It'll be simple,' he added finally.

'Except that you will have to remember to call me Emma.'

'I won't slip up,' he returned confidently.

'I must phone Emma when I get back to my flat. What she will say I do not know. She's always so wise and logical about everything.'

'You're afraid she'll say you are making a mistake?'

'She might. . . . I can't really imagine just how she will react,' added Caryl finally.

'I daresay she'll be pleased that you're settled. She'll be getting married herself soon, I expect.'

'Yes, she's going out to Patrick in Lagos.'

Brad made no further comment, and an hour and a half later he was dropping her at the dower house. This was at her request, as she wanted to go along to see Sandy before going over to the manor to present herself to Sir Geoffrey. Her feelings were mixed about that; she already had tinges of apprehension running along her spine in case she made a slip and gave the whole show away. Brad had said he would have a talk with Robert; he had also decided to have the announcement of their engagement put into the local newspaper. He was very businesslike about it all, and Caryl felt she was being manipulated, but although she went through a diversity of thoughts and emotions, she did admit, logically, that the marriage being in effect one of convenience as far as Brad was concerned, the attendant activities would naturally take a practical and unemotional course.

It was half past three when she arrived at the manor. The door was opened to her by James, who treated her with the kind of deference which told her that he knew she was to become the wife of his employer.

'Good afternoon, Miss Chapman.' He smiled. 'Mr. Craven told me to show you into the drawing room and to say he would not keep you waiting more than a few minutes. Is there anything I can get for you?'

'No, thank you,' she answered, having to make a tremendous effort to appear calm and collected.

She sat down and looked around with a totally different view of things than she had before. She was soon to be mistress here, able to switch the furniture around, to change the position of pictures and ornaments. . . . Or perhaps she would not have the temerity, fearing she might displease her husband. A sigh escaped her and tremors of doubt and uncertainty caused her nerves to tense, so that when Brad arrived she felt constrained—and cold, as if a draught of icy air had been trained upon her naked body.

'Ah, there you are!' Brad was as cool as ever, oozing confidence and self-assurance. 'You look charming in that suit. Does the colour have some exotic name?' he added with a hint of amusement in his eyes.

She shook her head, the tenseness seeping out of her. 'It's just a turquoise suit with a knife-pleated skirt.'

He laughed briefly. 'I'm learning,' he said and glanced at the clock on the wall. 'I have talked with Robert and also with my uncle. No need to tell you he is delighted.'

'I'm happy for him,' returned Caryl sincerely, and

then, more slowly: 'Robert . . . what did he say about our engagement?'

Brad looked at her intently through eyes that had narrowed a little. 'Well, seeing that you ask, he seemed rather taken aback—'

'But he was bound to be,' cut in Caryl swiftly, vexed by the fact that her colour had risen. She felt guilty under that all-examining stare yet did not know why she should. 'Everyone is going to be surprised.'

'He appeared to be disappointed.' Brad's expression was remote and a little unnerving. 'I must admit I was somewhat puzzled by his reaction.' A pause, but Caryl could find nothing to say. 'Has there been something between you?'

'Not anything—er—serious. We've been out for a meal a couple of times.'

'I see. . . .' A few seconds elapsed before he added, a stern, inflexible quality in his voice, 'You will not be going out with him from now on, Caryl. You do understand?'

She nodded rather absently, amazed to find that her pulses were drumming with anger. She resented his imperious manner. In fact, it was almost dictatorial. That firm little chin of hers had lifted, and the result was that his eyes had narrowed again, and there was a glint in them this time that warned her to take care.

'Yes, Brad,' she said, very reluctantly adopting a meek, submissive tone. 'I understand.' She frowned inwardly, aware of a keen sense of disappointment at not being able to go out with Robert again. She had been good for him and had hoped to continue helping him over his grief. He would be hurt by what had happened, feeling himself to be deprived of the comfort he was obviously hoping to get from his association with Caryl.

'Let us now go in and see Uncle.' Brad's voice had lost its stern inflection, and a half smile touched his lips. 'Take care, Caryl, for, as I said before, Uncle's sight might be impaired but his intellect certainly is not.'

The old man was sitting in the high-backed chair, but he moved as if excited when Caryl and Brad entered the room. Robert was there, standing by his chair, and as his eyes met those of Caryl she noticed a sort of pain in their depths. Her heart cried for him, and she was determined to see him alone at the first opportunity. He came forward with extended hand, and she heard his quiet words of congratulation. She answered, painfully aware of the stiffness in her voice and regretting her inability to banish it and appear more cordial and uninhibited. But what lay before her had become an ordeal, because she hated deceit in any form whatsoever. Yet she carried off the meeting with Sir Geoffrey in a way that brought her the highest praise from the man to whom she had become engaged.

'You were wonderful,' he told her when, later, they were in the drawing room having a cup of tea. Louisa had brought in the tray; Caryl had seen the girl's eyes widen in sheer disbelief on noticing the lovely ring, and she had had no time to recover her surprise—nor to wonder who had placed the ring there—before Brad said casually, 'Louisa, Miss Chapman and I have become engaged to be married.'

'Oh . . . !' The girl's mouth had moved convulsively, her eyes had become dark with intense dislike. The girl's feet seemed heavy on the carpet as she left the room, and it was as if a weight had descended upon her.

She would waste no time in phoning her idol, thought Caryl, then shut her mind to Marcia's reaction.

That she was shutting her mind to several important circumstances was with her all the time—for instance, there must be a good reason why Brad was acting as he was, giving Marcia up to marry someone he did not love. Caryl refused to dwell upon that reason. She preferred to bury her head in the sand, which was totally contrary to what her sister would have done. Emma liked everything open and aboveboard; she was not one for taking chances or making any move for which the outcome might be unpredictable.

'I must go now,' said Caryl when she had finished her tea. 'I want to phone Emma—' She broke off and grimaced. 'I shan't know how to begin.'

'She'll be coming down for the wedding?'

'I hope so—yes, she is bound to want to be my bridesmaid.'

'It won't be a big wedding,' warned Brad but went on to say it wouldn't be a hole-in-the-corner affair, either. 'Uncle will want a little fuss, so we shall pander to him.'

'I can have a white dress?' It was important suddenly that she should, because, later, she could look back and say that she had had the kind of wedding she had always wanted—a white flowing gown and orange blossoms, choirboys, and, of course, her sister in attendance.

Brad said they would have the reception in the large banquet hall of the manor rather than at an hotel, this after agreeing to her request for a white wedding dress. 'I'm afraid the number of guests doesn't really warrant the use of the hall, but Uncle will expect us to have the reception there.'

Caryl walked slowly back to her flat, her heart light

because the future looked so rosy and because she had given pleasure to an old man at the end of his life.

She telephoned Emma and told her the news, then waited in the long, disbelieving silence for her to speak.

At last Emma said, 'It's the very first time I have ever known you to be impulsive, Caryl. What the devil are you thinking about to marry without love?'

'Brad says it could come later.' Caryl felt foolish at making a comment like that, but she was lost for words.

Her sister's response was dry. 'Love usually comes first and then the marriage. You intend doing it the other way round. Unique.'

'Not unique; it's been done before.'

'Without success, then. No marriage can succeed unless based on love. Even then it's precarious these days, because for some as yet undiscovered reason love often dies, hence the large number of divorces.'

'Don't talk of divorce! I hate this attitude of yours, Emma!'

'On the defensive, are you? You might well be. I'm coming down right away to see if I can make you change your mind.'

'You won't do that. . . . Emma, are you still there . . . ?' Impatiently Caryl replaced the receiver that had gone dead on her. She hoped Emma would bring with her something suitable for the wedding!

Chapter Six

It was the following day that Caryl had the opportunity of seeing Robert. He was taking a stroll after lunch, while Sir Geoffrey was having a nap. Caryl left her flat to hurry after him and was a little breathless as she caught him up in a little glade where the trees were thick and the sunlight sparse.

'Hello, Caryl,' he greeted her, and she was gratified to see him produce a smile. 'Or should I not be so familiar now that you're to be the wife of my employer?'

'How are you?' she asked, ignoring his question. 'I've been watching out for you to explain everything.'

'You have no need to explain anything to me, Caryl.' He flicked a hand in invitation for her to sit down on a fallen tree trunk.

'Nevertheless, I intend to explain,' she began after sitting down and waiting for him to do the same.

'You're an intelligent young man, Robert, and so I wouldn't insult that intelligence by saying that Brad and I fell in love in minutes and decided to get married.'

He was nodding as she spoke, so she was not surprised to hear him say, 'I didn't think it was a love match. You're doing it for Sir Geoffrey?'

'Brad is.' Her quiet reply was not meant to hide anything, and Robert glanced sharply at her.

'You're in love with him?'

'I have been for years.' She smiled reflectively. 'He was engaged to my sister, but I wanted him desperately.' She paused a moment in hesitation. But she had become Robert's friend and confidante in a very short time and she knew that she in turn could confide in him, which she did, lifting her head to meet his eyes as she came to the end of her narrative. 'So you see, Robert, I could not refuse his offer of marriage, even though I am fully aware that at present he doesn't love me.'

'Have you thought about Marcia?'

'You mean, have I asked myself if he loved her? Yes, but I feel sure he didn't, Robert, because he's not the man to give up a girl he loves and marry one he doesn't just to please his uncle. I think you will agree with me about that.'

'Yes, I have to agree, but at the same time I feel there is another reason for his asking you to marry him.'

'I in turn agree' was Caryl's candid rejoinder. 'Yet I'm reluctant to dwell on it, because it will make me unhappy at a time in my life when I ought to be at my happiest.'

'What strange logic!' he exclaimed, but he was smiling as if in sympathy with her refusal to probe into something that would make her unhappy.

'You'll be meeting my sister,' Caryl told him after a

pause. 'She doesn't approve of my impulsiveness, but then she always follows what is practical. She has to see just where she is going before she takes even an initial step.'

'Very wise, but unfortunately there are few of us who are able to be like that. Tell me about her, Caryl; she sounds intriguing.'

'She's thirty—but I believe I've already told you that. She's very pretty—no, beautiful—and has the figure of a model.'

'You sound exceedingly proud of her,' returned Robert with a hint of amusement.

'I am. And we have always agreed so well despite the difference in ages. I am hoping to talk her round over this impulsiveness of mine,' ended Caryl with a laugh.

'You and I shan't be going out together anymore, of course.' Robert changed the subject abruptly, a trace of sadness in his voice. 'I was beginning to look forward to forming a strong friendship with you.'

'We shall still be friends,' she assured him. 'But, as you say, we can't go out to the café.' She paused a moment. 'I intend to spend an hour or so with Sir Geoffrey every day, if it's all right with you, so we shall see each other quite often.'

Robert nodded but gave a small sigh. She could guess what his thoughts were. He was regretting the loss of her company for a meal on his evenings off, and she decided to ask Brad if he could dine with them sometimes. She said as the thought struck her, 'Does Brad know about Mary?'

'No. I've not told anyone here about her except you.'

'Do you mind if I tell him?'

For a moment he pondered and then, 'Not really. Have you some reason?'

'Yes, but I shall not tell you what it is yet.' She smiled.

He did not press her, and after a while they came from the glade and walked together back to the dower house, where she stood outside the door until he was lost to view. Then, sadly, she went inside, unable to think of anything but the fact that she could not now dine out with Robert and give him that lift which seemed to have brightened his life and relieved him just a little from the burden of his sorrow. Well, she was resolved to talk to Brad and see what he would suggest. Caryl hoped he would agree to invite Robert to join them on his evenings off duty. He had invited Robert to dine at the manor once, she recalled optimistically.

Emma arrived late that afternoon. She had earlier telephoned to say what time she would be in Dorchester, and Caryl had asked Brad if she could borrow the smaller of his cars so that she could meet her sister at the railway station. Brad had been agreeable and off she had gone, her heart beginning to beat unevenly as she drew in to the station and pulled up alongside another car which had obviously come for another passenger. She couldn't bear the idea of quarrelling with Emma but knew she would not tolerate any interference in her plans. She meant to marry Brad, and that was that. The train drew in, and then the sisters were locked in a hug before getting into the car and driving away. Emma talked then, wanting to know every detail of what had transpired. Slanting her a glance as she mentioned Marcia, Caryl saw the sudden frown that creased her sister's brow.

'I don't like that for a start,' stated Emma forcefully. 'Why should he jilt her when the marriage was almost—?'

'He hasn't jilted her!' Caryl's voice was urgent and tinged with a defensive note. 'You talk as if I've stolen Brad from her.'

'It's obvious you haven't done that,' returned Emma mildly, 'because you didn't go after him in any way at all . . . or did you?' Emma evinced faint amusement as she added the question.

'Certainly not!' Caryl was well away from the station now and heading for the main road to Bridport. Traffic was fairly heavy, and for a while she was having to concentrate, with the result that a silence fell between the two sisters.

'What is this Marcia like?' Emma asked with interest once the car was purring smoothly along the tree-lined road, the town having been left behind. 'Beautiful, I suppose, and with all the polish which the wife of Brad ought to have. I don't expect you have given that a thought, have you?' said Emma, diverting from her question.

'The polish, you mean? Well, you were once going to marry him, weren't you?'

'I have more self-confidence than you. Being the lady of the manor would have been the kind of challenge that would appeal to me; it would have been a challenge which I'd have met without flinching.'

'What makes you think I can't do the same?' Caryl had pulled up at a traffic light, and she turned to stare at her sister's profile. 'I am twenty-four, remember—not a child.'

'Tell me about this Marcia,' said Emma again. 'Does she know of your engagement?'

'I expect she does.' Caryl told Emma about Louisa, saying she felt sure the girl would have lost no time in informing Marcia of what had happened.

'Brad should have been the one to tell her.'

'He probably did tell her, but I'll bet she already knew, from Louisa.' Caryl let out the clutch as the lights changed, and the car purred forward past a slow starter. 'Marcia's beautiful and extremely sophisticated,' she went on presently. 'I must admit that she would make the ideal wife for Brad, but she's hard inside and spiteful. Brad was only looking at the lovely surface, not at what was underneath.'

'Men are like that.' Emma shrugged with disgust. 'They always believe in their own cleverness and perception, but they're a lot of fools where women are concerned. As you say, they look only on the surface, so they miss what's beneath.'

'You sound as if you've become cynical.'

'Not at all. But I've always regarded men as fools—most men, that is.'

'But not Patrick,' said Caryl with a laugh.

'Not Patrick," agreed Emma, then brought back the subject of Caryl's intention of marrying Brad. 'You admit you're in love with him but that he's not in love with you. What kind of marriage is that? What will your—er—honeymoon be like?'

Caryl was glad of the darkness of the car and road, because she knew the colour had leapt to her face. 'There won't be one.'

'And you sound dejected about it!'

'Naturally. I want to be Brad's wife in every way.' She was speeding without knowing, and Emma said something to make her ease off a bit. 'The honeymoon might come later.'

'Might? Caryl, you can't do this! I shall talk to Brad, tell him what I think of him for asking you—'

'Do that, and I shall never speak to you again,' broke

in Caryl hotly. 'He doesn't know I love him—please keep that in mind!'

'Sorry. After all, it's really none of my business. When is this farcical marriage to take place?'

'Don't be like that,' pleaded Caryl, ready to cry. 'I don't know when it will take place, but it's to be soon.'

'In case the old man should die and miss it all, eh?'

'I hate your talking like this. It's not you, Emma!'

'I want to make you see sense and not rush into something you could come to regret. This haste—it isn't right!'

'Emma,' said Caryl softly, 'I want to marry Brad—more than I have ever wanted anything in my life. If I am making a mistake, it is only I who will suffer, and I'm willing to take the chance.'

'Crazy!' snapped Emma and lapsed into silence for a while. When eventually she spoke, it was to ask about Caryl's ring.

'I forgot to put it on. I've not become used to the idea yet.'

She heard Emma draw a breath and bit her lip. Would she ever come round to her way of thinking? Would she realise just how she, Caryl, felt about Brad? If only Emma could understand, then all her objections would dissolve. She said after a while, 'Have you brought a dress suitable for the wedding?'

'Of course I haven't! It won't take place tomorrow, will it?'

Caryl ignored that as she said quietly, 'I expect it will be in about a week's time. I want you for my bridesmaid, naturally.'

'You mean, it's to be a proper wedding?'

'Proper? What do you mean?'

'Church and flowers and a party afterwards?'

'What else?' asked Caryl tautly. 'Did you expect us to call at the registrar's office in town and have a ten-minute session with him?' She was approaching another set of lights and slowed down; they changed before she reached them and she revved up again.

'As a matter of fact,' admitted Emma, 'that's exactly what I envisaged.'

'I'm having a white dress and all that goes with it. The reception will be in the large hall of the manor.'

'Oh, well, at least that sounds a bit more civilised than I'd imagined,' said Emma, mollified to some extent.

'I shall probably be going for my dress tomorrow, so if you come with me you can get yours at the same time.'

'You want me to stay for a week, then?'

'It's either that or go home and come back, which is silly. It isn't as if you've anything much to do at the kennels now.'

'As a matter of fact, I finished yesterday. I'm out of work.'

'When are you planning to go to Nigeria?'

'In about a fortnight. I'm putting all our stuff in storage—or at least I was. There isn't much of yours, though, so you might either want to sell it or bring it here.'

'It can come here—and yours also, if you like. It would save the cost of storing it.'

'I shall take you up on that.' Emma glanced around and said, 'We're almost there; it's becoming familiar. If I'd never met Patrick, I might just be regretting throwing all the luxury away.'

Caryl said nothing. She was turning into the long avenue, and dusk was not so far away. The trees overhead almost hid the sky—a cobalt sky with drifting clouds and one lone star twinkling through the fluttering leaves.

'I didn't ask if Brad has changed much.' Emma was getting out of the car as she spoke.

'You asked me after I'd been on that one-day visit.'

'Ah, yes, I forgot. He's still as handsome but greying a little, and he's collected a few lines, I think you said.'

'You'll see for yourself in a few minutes.' Caryl was opening the boot of the car to take out Emma's suitcase, but at that moment the front door opened and James was there, ready to take the case and to show the girls into the drawing room. Caryl graciously drew his attention to her sister; he bowed his head in recognition and went off to tell Brad they had arrived.

Caryl watched curiously and with a strange sense of detachment as the two met and shook hands. Brad looked Emma over and she did likewise, smiling as she said, 'You haven't changed much, Brad.'

'Nor have you, Emma.' Cool the tone, but he was interested in the girl he had once desired to marry. Caryl wondered if this situation was unique and felt it must be—with one sister here as bridesmaid to the girl who was going to marry the man to whom she had once been engaged. 'We must have a chat later. Meanwhile, I'll get Louisa to show you your room. I take it you will be spending your time at Caryl's flat, but, as she has no extra sleeping accommodation, you'll be staying here at night.' Caryl had already mentioned this to Emma, so it came as no surprise to her.

Louisa's face was a study when Brad said, 'Take Miss Chapman's sister to the room you've prepared.'

'Are you coming with me?' Emma asked, and Caryl nodded at once. The suitcase was already there, brought up by James, and Louisa asked stiffly if she should unpack it. Emma said no and dismissed the girl with an abrupt 'You may go.' Then, to Caryl: 'I'd get rid of her if I were you, or she'll be carrying tales to this Marcia woman. You don't want her to know you're not sleeping together.'

Caryl turned away to hide her reddened cheeks, and Emma went into the bathroom. Staring through the window, Caryl dwelt on Emma's words. Yes, somehow she must get rid of Louisa . . . but in what way could this be done? It certainly did not seem right to bring about her dismissal—presupposing that was possible—on the mere assumption that she would carry tales to her former mistress. And in any case she, Caryl, could not dismiss her without consulting Brad, and if she did that she would have to have some valid complaint against the girl.

Emma came back into the bedroom, and the two girls unpacked her clothes and hung them up in the wardrobe.

'Are you happier about my marriage?' Caryl had to ask just before they went down to the drawing room again.

'I suppose I shall have to be,' answered Emma, but with a sigh. 'Let us hope that it turns out all right in the end.'

The wedding went off without a hitch. Caryl was the glowing bride; her sister, too, came in for much admiration, for she seemed almost regal in her oyster-pink dress of lace and net. Brad seemed detached, aloof, but did the right thing by kissing the bride and then her sister. About thirty guests attended the reception, among whom were all those people who had been at the dinner party. Robert was there, and Sir Geoffrey, of course. He seemed to have gained a little strength, because he was walking very well, guided by the watchful Robert. He had been introduced to Emma, who had to be Caryl, the bride's sister and attendant. It was a rather tense moment for both sisters—and perhaps Brad, too—when Emma had met the old man, because he might just have found something in her voice which would have set him thinking, but all went off very well.

And at last it was over, with all the guests gone and Emma having decided to occupy Caryl's flat for the night and leave before lunch the following day.

'Well, how do you feel, Caryl?' Brad was handing her a drink as they stood in the drawing room, Caryl beautiful and serene in her lovely wedding gown. 'Tired, I think.'

Her smile was almost tender. She knew what she wanted but knew also that it was not for tonight—no, nor tomorrow or the next night. . . . But sometime perhaps.

'A little,' she admitted. 'It's been a wonderful day, Brad.'

His eyes were curiously intent and examining. 'You don't mind that it's not as it should be?'

'I knew what I was doing.'

'I hope you'll be happy.' He raised his glass and said, 'Let us just drink to the future and whatever it might hold for us.'

There was promise in his words, and happily she lifted her glass to let it touch his.

Only two days later Caryl was shopping in Dorchester when a motorcyclist swept through the stoplight at a crossing and knocked her off her feet. Within seconds a crowd had gathered, and although Caryl was sure she was not badly hurt, the ambulance arrived to take her to the hospital. Less than an hour later her husband was at her bedside, his face drawn with anxiety.

'Oh, Brad. . . .' She smiled at him, rather wanly because by now she was suffering from shock and felt much worse than she had immediately after the accident. 'They're making such a fuss—what with the X rays and the horrid drinks to steady my nerves.'

'You've been very lucky—' He broke off, and Caryl became fascinated by the pulsing of a nerve in his temple.

'You've been worried about me?'

'Caryl, dear, of course I've been worried. What a question to ask! However, what's more important is how you are feeling. I've been assured by the doctor that nothing's broken, but that you are suffering from shock, which is understandable.' He turned his head as the door of the private ward opened and the doctor came in. Tall and slender, with broad square shoulders, he wore an air of authority almost equal to that of Brad himself. He asked Brad to leave with him when, after feeling Caryl's pulse and resting a cool hand on her brow, he made to go again. When eventually Brad returned, he said that she would be in hospital for two or three days, and after that he was taking her away for a holiday.

'You are?' In spite of how she was feeling, she experienced a little access of pleasure and excitement at the prospect of a holiday with her husband. 'Where to?'

He shook his head at that and said they would decide later. 'It's at the doctor's suggestion,' he added. 'He's of the opinion that a complete change and a rest are necessary.'

'Necessary?' She frowned.

'It seems that a period of deep depression could follow even a small accident like the one you were involved in. We don't want that, so I shall take you away.'

She was thoughtful after he had left. Sir Geoffrey had had to be told, Brad had said, and Caryl wished they would not keep her here. She wanted more than anything to reassure the old man that she was all right. For the past week she had spent an hour with him each day, and it had been no hardship. He was interesting to talk to and happy in her company. She felt the gratification of giving pleasure, and although she wanted more than anything to go on holiday with Brad, she did consider the old man's feelings and decided to ask Brad to make the holiday fairly short.

When Brad came the following day, he said he had booked them to go to the Bahamas for a fortnight.

'That's a long time to be away from Uncle,' she protested and went on quickly in case she should be misunderstood, 'I'd love to have two weeks, Brad, but I've been going in to Uncle every day and he'll miss me.' And there was Sandy, too, she thought.

Brad nodded understandingly, much to her relief. 'I'll phone the travel agency and make it a week, then.'

They left the following Saturday, flying to Miami, and then, after a tedious wait at the airport, they took the half-hour flight to Grand Bahama Island, to be met by sultry, humid heat and brilliant sunshine. After unpacking in their adjoining rooms at the hotel, they had a late dinner and went to bed. The next day was spent swimming or relaxing on the beach, but somehow Caryl felt restless, aware she was not enjoying the break as much as she should have been doing. She tried to thrust the reason from her mind, but it was useless to deny that she would have loved this to be their honeymoon. It was a idyllic setting; the hotel was romantic, with flowers and plants everywhere and subdued lighting in the lounges and restaurant. It was uncrowded, too, since this was the time of the year when many people kept away because of the heat.

'What's wrong?' Brad asked her when, halfway through the week, they had decided to dine at the Ruby Restaurant, a most attractive eating place with a view of the golf course with its belts of exotic trees and its smooth, sweeping fairways and velvet-soft greens. 'You seem to be a little depressed.' He sounded anxious, she thought as she heard him add, 'I don't want that to happen, Caryl. The doctor at the hospital stressed to me the consequences which could result from your falling into a deep depression.'

She looked swiftly at him, and leaping into her mind was the case of a friend of her stepmother who had suffered a small injury after being knocked down by a car. Ever since she had been in and out of a mental hospital, and her husband was nearly out of his mind with worry which had now become incessant. Caryl could not by any stretch of imagination see herself in a state like that, but obviously her husband was greatly troubled by what the doctor had said.

'I don't think there is any fear of my falling into a deep depression,' she said confidently.

'But there's something the matter with you at present.'

'I admit I feel a little down, but it'll pass. Please don't worry about me, Brad. I promise you I shall made a supreme effort to buck up.' She saw him frown at that, and only then did she realise how ill phrased her words had been.

After dinner they walked on the golf course, with the night air cool and crystal clear, scented by pines and the mingling of flower perfumes. A crescent moon rode high in the clear purple dome of the heavens, and the constellations floated all around it. A night for romance . . . and she a new bride. . . .

She glanced at her husband and caught her breath. Tall and spare and dangerously masculine, he was so desirable to her at this moment that she found herself rebelling against the conventions which gave exclusively to a man the prerogative of approach. Why couldn't *she* tell *him* what was in her mind? Why couldn't she stop, here beneath the rosy glow of the lamp set in the tall coconut palm, and put her arms around him, kiss him passionately until she had aroused his emotions, awakened his desire for her? Conscious of her attention, Brad slanted her a glance. He smiled, and her heart seemed to melt.

'It's—a beautiful n-night,' she stammered, blushing at the possibility of his reading her thoughts. Which was absurd in the extreme, she instantly chided herself.

'Indeed it is.' He sounded content and happy. She felt, with a little shock of surprise and pleasure, his hand seek hers and the strong fingers curl around it. Silently they walked along a fairway towards a delightful pool where giant water lilies floated on the starlit surface. West Indian music drifted out to them from the steel band playing in the restaurant; cicadas made a very different kind of music, and from somewhere on the side of the pool the croaking of frogs provided its own particular chorus.

Brad stopped and looked down into her face; she wondered if he were as deeply affected by their surroundings as she. It was magical, the idyllic setting for love. . . .

Quietly he drew her to him, and his lips were gentle on her eager mouth. The kiss was brief; he slid his fingers into her hair to bring her head against his chest. She closed her eyes, content to stay quietly in his arms even while wondering why neither of them spoke. She quivered when his hand beneath her chin imperiously brought her head up, and ripples of excitement ran along her spine as he bent his head again to capture her softly parted lips. His embrace became stronger as she pressed her slender body close to his and she knew the thrill of his muscles rippling and becoming tightened against her. His hands began to rove over her, possessive and strong and determined to tempt. His fingers on her breast began with a feather-light caress that set every nerve end on fire by its tantalising finesse, and when presently they closed upon the nipple she uttered a tiny moan of rapture and arched her pliant frame in a sort of urgent, desperate attempt to meld its feminine softness with the rocklike strength of his thighs. She felt exalted when his breathing became uneven, and her cup of happiness was complete when she heard him say in a throaty bass tone, 'Let us go in, Caryl, to collect your wrap. It's time we were back at the hotel.'

She had showered and slipped into a diaphanous nightgown when she heard the gentle tap on the bedroom door. She sped across the room to open it, then blushed at her eagerness. A bride should be shy—and indeed she suddenly did feel shy, turning away abruptly from the tall man in the dark blue dressing gown and taking up the hairbrush which lay on the exquisite Queen Anne dressing table. A low laugh broke the silence of the room; she heard the door close firmly, the key click in the lock. The brush was taken from her trembling fingers and laid down. Brad turned her to face him, stared into her eyes for a long moment before bending his dark head to take her lips in a long, possessive kiss that left her breathless.

'How beautiful you are. . . .' His mouth was warm and moist against her cheek; it moved to possess her lips again, this time with the added strength and urgency of his need for her. A sort of gentle savagery mingled with tenderness, mastery with a kind of reverence which was reflected in his experienced caresses as his long brown hands roamed over her, from her graceful white throat to her breasts and down to rest upon her stomach, as if he were deriving supreme pleasure from the sharp and swift contraction of the muscles in response to his touch. Caryl waited in breathless, quivering expectation as very slowly his hand slid farther, fingers spread . . . and then his passion flared, an erupting volcano which drew his wife helplessly into its fiery depths, igniting her own passion, and for several ecstatic moments their eager bodies swayed in primitive abandon and desire. She thrilled to the granite hardness of his thighs, powerful and dominating against the feminine softness of her own body, to the mastery of his lips, the near arrogance of his possessive hands as they slid down her spine to caress her curves. At last he held her from him and smiled at her heightened colour. Her pulses were still drumming, her heartbeat racing. She lifted a hand to flick hair from her forehead; Brad caught it and brought it to his lips.

'What an enchanting little creature you are. . . .' His voice was thick, his breathing uneven, and it seemed to Caryl that his hand was unsteady as he brought it to her face, his fingers tracing the line of her cheek before tilting her face by their pressure beneath her chin; his mouth was feather-light against her ear, but tantalising, and a quiver shot through her body as desire flared again. For long moments she knew the rapture of his love play before, holding her from him again, he slid his hands beneath the shoulder straps of her nightgown; her flesh tingled at his touch, her cheeks coloured as the dainty garment fell to the floor around her feet. He looked at her, taking his fill of the slender beauty of her youthful form. He shook his head, and she would have given anything to know his thoughts. But suddenly she was crushed to him, every nerve sensitised by the knowledge of her appeal as she pressed to him, arching her naked body in a sort of primitive supplication to his demands.

Gently he lifted her and carried her to the bed. She managed a smile as he laid her down and stood for a space staring into her eyes. And then he was beside her, his strong arms about her, his naked body pressed against hers, his demanding mouth forcing her lips apart so that she could experience the quivering ecstasy of his exploring tongue. She caressed him—his face and throat, his nape as she slid her hands into his hair, joining him in his love play until the final act of fulfilment transported them both to the topmost heights of rapture.

Chapter Seven

Caryl was awake early the following morning, and a slow and lovely smile came to her lips and hovered there as memory rushed in, helped by the sleeping figure of her husband, his bronzed face starkly contrasting with the dazzling whiteness of the pillow. She kissed him and ruffled his hair and then jumped out of bed when he would have grabbed her.

'What game, my little one?' Mock severity in his voice as he came to her and gave her a playful slap. 'You will soon learn not to tempt me if you're not willing to take the consequences.' And he lifted her into his arms and walked slowly back to the bed. Soon his breathing was ragged as his avid hands explored. Caryl's arms slid around his neck, her fingers tantalisingly light as they caressed his nape and then his earlobe. Passion flared, and the suffocating pounding of Caryl's heart felt almost like a physical pain. But it was gone within seconds as her body and his strained together, then became melded in the sublime intimacy of fulfilment.

It was later, when they faced one another across the breakfast table, that Brad said with a hint of amusement, 'The platonic marriage didn't last long, did it? Have you any regrets?'

'None,' she answered, happiness giving a sparkle to her eyes.

'You were a provocative little wretch.'

'And what of you?' she countered. 'Are you trying to say it was only I who tempted?'

'The female is always the one who does the tempting.' He was teasing her, and she laughed. Life was good! She glanced around at the immediate scene of long, flower-adorned veranda on which the breakfast tables were set, at the indigo water of the swimming pool with its surround of flowers and rocks and the sparkling cascade glistening in the morning sunshine. In the distance the smooth waters of the ocean were indigo and aquamarine—the perfect foil for the white-sailed luxury yachts basking in graceful elegance, or moving gently in the zephyr of a breeze. There were a few people using the pool and a few more reclining in loungers, but numbers were small at this time of the year, and Caryl liked it this way; she hated crowds and noise and any kind of loud, unruly behaviour.

'Have you nothing to say in your defence?' Brad's voice cut into her reverie, and she laughed again.

'I prefer to wait until the time comes for me to challenge you,' she said.

'And suppose there is no occasion when a challenge will be appropriate?' His voice was low and strangely brooding all at once, and she was startled by it. Nerves tingled, doubts rose like a cloud that shut out the warmth of the sun. Was he already regretting last night . . . and this morning? It didn't make sense, and yet . . . His eyes were vacant, as if his thoughts were far away, and reluctantly Caryl's thoughts turned to Marcia, the girl whom everyone had believed he would marry. But he had married her, Caryl, instead, and he maintained he had done it for his uncle. Caryl was sure that was part of the reason . . . but, like Robert, she knew there was an altogether different reason why he had thrown Marcia over and married someone else.

But what reason?

'That is a strange thing to say,' she murmured at last, looking straight at him across the table. 'You sound as if—as if we—you don't intend our new relationship to—to be permanent.' It was difficult to get the words out, but she had to know. He frowned and his mouth tightened, but when he spoke his voice was infinitely gentle.

'You obviously want it to be permanent, Caryl.'

'Of course.' She shook her head dazedly. 'We can't do that—be together, I mean—and then decide not to be together again. It would be neither possible nor natural.' Was she pleading? The idea was unpleasant because she was not without her share of pride.

'Then it shall be permanent.' Reaching out, he covered her hand with his. 'Perhaps Uncle will see the heir he wanted, after all.'

She coloured, saw the thread of laughter in his eyes, and spoke hastily, just for something to say. 'You felt he'd not live longer than about six months.'

Brad nodded his head. 'It could be a little longer,' he said, 'or it could be less. One never can predict in a case like Uncle's.'

After that the conversation changed, veered deliberately by Brad, to whom the matter of his uncle's health was painful. But although Brad swam with her and strolled along the beach, his way with her seemed to be a pose, a veneer concealing an altogether different frame of mind. Caryl could not help but be conscious of it, and repeatedly her thoughts would switch to Marcia . . . the girl who unknowingly was spoiling her honeymoon.

That evening she and Brad dined and danced, then wandered along a lonely palm-fringed beach where white sand glittered like diamonds in the silver light from a full moon. She wanted Brad to hold her hand, to reassure her by the gesture that his thoughts were with his wife and no one else.

He did not hold her hand, but his lovemaking was all she could have desired when, later, they were together, bodies warm and naked against each other. And when the tumult had died, replaced by the blissful sense of absolute contentment, his good-night kiss was tender and long, his hand on her breast reverent and warm.

The week ended all too swiftly, and the last morning found them wandering among the most gloriously exotic flowers in the Garden of the Groves, a spectacularly landscaped region of botanical perfection. And in the garden stood a small chapel where marriages could take place. Mainly, though, marriages planned to take place in the Garden of the Groves were conducted out in the open, among the flowers and with the sun showering its brilliance on bride and groom and guests.

'It must be wonderful to be married in a place like this!' exclaimed Caryl when they came to the clearing where stood a tall white arched construction. 'Just imagine how unique it would be!'

'Unique?' With a lift of Brad's brows. 'How can it be unique when lots of people do it?'

She laughed, then stopped abruptly as four brightly dressed young men came into view. 'A steel band! Is there going to be a wedding, do you think?'

'Could be, but I have no intention of standing here to wait for it.'

'Oh . . . I'd love to see it, Brad.'

'It'll be some time before it takes place.'

But already the musicians were getting ready to play, and then there appeared the priest, clad in white robes which contrasted dramatically with his black face. The musicians were also Bahamians, and then the couple arrived and they, too, were black.

'Please stay,' begged Caryl, aware that several other people, attracted by the activity, had stopped to watch. Brad shrugged and seemed resigned. Caryl's spirits were damped by his lack of enthusiasm, but she did not suggest they move on. Brad could not always expect to have everything his own way!

'The ceremony's about to start. Look, Brad, at the little ones. Don't they look pretty?'

'Very.'

'And the bride—she looks so young.'

Brad did not comment, and they watched the ceremony in silence. Nevertheless, to Caryl it was a novel experience, and she enjoyed it. The steel band music echoed through the gardens as the couple, followed by their numerous relatives and friends, began to walk slowly away, making for the nearby hotel in which the reception was to be held.

Brad was obviously relieved when it was all over, and in the taxi which took them back to their hotel he retained his silence.

'Is anything wrong?' Caryl had to ask when, after lunch, they were in their room packing for the evening flight home.

'What should be the matter?'

'You've been so quiet all morning, and even over lunch you scarcely had the patience to answer me when I spoke.'

'I'm sorry.' He came towards her with outstretched hands. 'I've a great deal on my mind, Caryl, so bear with me, dear.'

She looked at him, at the bronzed unsmiling face, and knew without any doubt at all that he'd had difficulty in concealing his impatience beneath the words he had uttered. They were forced, and a great wave of depression swept over her as she moved away from him. A few days ago the future had seemed so rosy, but now . . .

The first thing she did on arrival home was to go and see Sandy. It was only half past nine in the morning, so she had no qualms at not going in to Sir Geoffrey first. He would not be ready for her for at least an hour and a half.

'Has Sandy been keeping well?' she inquired of Avice.

'Yes, very, and he didn't seem to fret for you at all.'

'Good. It's because he's become used to you, Avice.'

The girl merely shrugged and went away. She had become even more remote and quiet now that Caryl was married to her employer. Perhaps it was as it should be, thought Caryl, knowing that her husband would certainly expect the kennel-girls—and everyone else, for that matter—to assume a respectful attitude towards his wife.

Caryl was about to leave the kennels when she suddenly stiffened and stood still, waiting for the girl whose arrogant bearing would have told Caryl who she was even had she been little more than a figure in the far distance. Nerves rioted, a circumstance which angered Caryl because she knew that had it been Emma standing here she would have been more than ready for the girl.

'So you're back from your—er—honeymoon?' The sneer was pitted with venom, the eyes dark with hate. 'Did you have separate rooms as you do here?'

A rush of colour leapt to Caryl's cheeks. She groped for words, but all that came forth was 'Louisa's been carrying tales—' And then she stopped, humiliated beyond bearing by her own words. Why, oh, why couldn't she have hit back?

'So you admit it.' Marcia's laugh was like a rasp scraping every nerve cell in Caryl's body. 'I couldn't believe you'd be fool enough to marry him—no, not even after he had told me you and he were engaged! What reason did he give for wanting to marry you?' She stopped and waited, but there was no reply from Caryl. 'Do you know why he married you? I'll tell you, you little fool! He did it for spite, because he'd overheard something I'd said to a friend of mine.' Again she stopped, and although Caryl still remained silent, her interest had been caught, and her torturer knew it. But Marcia was now like some wild creature, her control almost gone. 'He overheard me saying I had him on a string! That I could twist him around my little finger! He knew it was true, knew he was madly in love with me, but when he heard that, he went straight off and proposed to you, just to get even with me, to show me I was wrong!' Marcia's face was twisted with wrath, her voice the snarl of an animal as she went on. 'But I wasn't wrong, and he knew it all the time. He was besotted with love for me and still is—'

'Stop!' cried Caryl, unable any longer to hear her husband spoken of in this manner. 'Besotted! What an expression to use! I was told you were capable of ridiculing Brad behind his back—'

'He deserved it! His arrogance had to be broken! I had no intention of marrying him until I'd moulded him—'

'Moulded!' It was Caryl's turn to laugh, almost hysterically 'You really believed you could mould a man like Brad? You must be crazy! Neither man nor woman could tell Brad what to do!'

'The big he-man, eh?' Marcia's mouth curved in a sneer, but it was her eyes that held Caryl fascinated, for they held a wild glitter, as if their owner were becoming unbalanced. 'You always did strike me as an insipid, cringing type who'd let a man walk all over you! Well, you'll see how long Brad will put up with that!'

'Obviously he didn't intend putting up with you!' Caryl shot at her. 'Did you seriously believe you could dictate to him?'

'He loves me, and because of it he'll do anything for me!'

'Except marry you.'

'He will, in the end. This farce is merely the result of his temper on hearing me say what I did. Mark my words, girl, he'll be asking for a divorce within a month!' Marcia's voice was now a high-pitched shriek, and instinctively Caryl put her hands to her ears. 'A month, do you hear! So make the most of it while you can!'

'Go away,' cried Caryl, every moment that passed

increasing the tumult within her. 'Go away and don't come back! You're trespassing on our land!'

For a terrible moment Caryl truly believed the girl would make a physical attack on her, and she braced herself for it. But Marcia's heaving body merely swayed for a second or two, and then she swung round and began to run, totally out of control.

'Thank God!' Drained and weak from the encounter, Caryl leant against the wire mesh of Sandy's cage, her whole system affected by the devastating experience through which she had passed. And as her nerves sobered so her mind was able to function, and now it was misery that engulfed her, clawing at her throat, pressing down on her body. She knew why Brad had married her . . . knew the 'other' reason which had puzzled her and which Robert had been aware of, too.

Should she tackle her husband? Caryl felt she must, for it seemed almost impossible to keep this knowledge to herself. And what of Louisa? Well, there was now a valid reason for dismissing her, and Caryl went straight to Brad's study and knocked on the door.

'Come in.' Brad looked up from the perusal of some papers on his desk and a frown came to his brow. 'What is it, Caryl?' he asked curtly, and immediately threw her off balance by his attitude. 'I'm exceedingly busy at the present time.'

She hesitated, saw his impatience increase as his fingers tapped restlessly on the desk. This was certainly not the time for troubling him with complaints about Louisa, and much less for having a showdown over the reason for his marrying her.

'If you're busy, then I'll talk later,' she said, a trifle bewildered by the sudden knowledge that she was not quite sure now whether she wanted a showdown or not.

Perhaps this little respite was fate's way of giving her more time to consider. She had believed she must have it out with Brad, but now she felt she ought to guard against impulsiveness, because the last thing she wanted was a rift between her husband and herself. Perhaps he did still love Marcia, but Caryl felt absolutely sure he would never seek a divorce in order to marry her, no matter what Marcia believed to the contrary. 'I'm sorry I troubled you,' she murmured turning to the door.

Brad spoke as she reached it. 'Perhaps you can tell me about it over lunch.'

She nodded her head absently. 'Perhaps,' she returned briefly and went out, closing the door quietly behind her.

When a short while later she went in to see Sir Geoffrey, he seemed far weaker than when she had left him eight days ago after spending rather longer than usual with him. She glanced at Robert, her eyes seeking some sign of anxiety on his face. It was tense, and the almost imperceptible nod of his head spoke volumes, as did the tiny sigh that escaped him.

'Did you have a wonderful holiday, my dear?' The old man's voice was husky and low; his eyes were peering as if their owner were desperate to see his companion's face. A great surge of pity welling up inside her completely erased the scar of her own troubles, if only temporarily.

'Yes, Uncle, it was marvellous!' Deliberately she injected a note of brightness into her voice. 'We both had a wonderful time.' She glanced at Robert, saw his eyes shadow, and an added pain invaded her heart.

'Your honeymoon . . . come closer to me, Emma.'

'I'm here, Uncle—very close.' She laid her hand over his and pressed it gently.

'Tell me about the Bahamas. Are you very brown with all that sun?'

'Yes, both Brad and I are.'

'Brad was in a few minutes ago, but he had things to do. He's coming in for a while after lunch as usual.' He paused and seemed to be gulping for air. Caryl bit her lip and looked at Robert. He was troubled but seemed resigned. Was Sir Geoffrey really nearing his end, then? Despite his age, it was to Caryl a depressing thought.

'I'll tell you about the holiday,' she said, again adding a bright note to her voice. 'Do you want to know about the flight first?'

'I want to know everything.'

Caryl began to talk, but something in Robert's manner made her hurry through the narrative, and she had barely finished when Robert came forward from his place by the window and said quietly, 'I think Emma had better leave now, sir. I suggest you have a little rest before your lunch.'

'I'm sure you are right, Robert,' agreed the old man. 'Though I am loath to have my niece-in-law leave me yet. You'll be back, Emma, dear?'

'Tomorrow,' inserted Robert firmly, but gently too. 'If Mr. Craven is to come, then that will be enough for today.'

'He's a tyrant,' complained Sir Geoffrey.

'But he knows what's good for you, Uncle.'

'What's good is not always the most pleasant.'

Caryl rose from her chair, then stooped to kiss the wrinkled cheek. 'I'll come tomorrow,' she promised, and a moment or so later she was in the little hallway listening to Robert saying flatly, 'It won't be long now, Caryl. I'm sending for the doctor later today.'

'How long?'

Robert shook his head. 'Not more than a couple of weeks—or perhaps three,' he amended.

'I shall leave you to tell Brad,' she said with a deep sigh.

'The doctor will do that, I expect.' Robert paused a moment. 'I suppose a miracle could happen and Sir Geoffrey could buck up. He has done so before, but this time . . .' Again he shook his head. 'This time I feel it is final.'

'It's so sad.'

He looked down into her face and a frown came suddenly to his brow. 'There seems to be more than sadness about you today, Caryl.' His eyes examined her in a close scrutiny and the frown remained. Caryl had started at his perception and then turned away. To her surprise Robert took her face in his hand and brought it round again. 'Something's happened,' he observed. 'You can confide in me; you know that.'

She nodded dumbly, and almost without being aware of her action she had covered his hand with her own. They had forgotten that the door was open. It led into the main hall of the manor, and just at that moment Brad came striding along from his study. Seeing them, he stopped abruptly, his dark eyes widening in anger and disbelief. 'What—'

'Brad!' Caryl drew away, hot colour mounting her cheeks. 'I—'

'What the devil's going on?' he demanded wrathfully. 'Caryl, you're supposed to be with Uncle!'

'I'm just coming away,' she began when Robert interrupted her to explain, in his customary cool and quiet manner. 'It was my fault, Mr. Craven. I was trying to comfort your wife. You see, I had just told her that Sir Geoffrey's condition is deteriorating rapidly and that I believe he has only about three weeks at the most to live.' He had left part of it out, but he had carried off the situation cleverly, and Caryl secretly congratulated him. In any case, the information he had imparted was more than sufficient to divert her husband's mind. She saw the anger in his eyes dissolve as sadness took its place.

'You're sure, Robert?' he said in a hollow sort of tone.

'I'm having the doctor in this afternoon, but—yes, Mr. Craven, I feel sure Sir Geoffrey is nearing his end.'

Neither Caryl nor Brad spoke as they walked together through the hall, and even when they parted at the bottom of the stairs Brad's only comment was 'I'll see you at lunch.'

And it was at lunch that Caryl said, in answer to Brad's question as to why she had wanted to see him earlier, 'I wondered if we could have Robert to dinner on his evenings off. He doesn't have any company at those times, and . . .' Her voice trailed off into silence as she noticed his changing expression. 'If you are willing to listen,' she persevered after a pause, 'then I can explain more fully.'

'Do so, by all means,' he invited, and the coolness in his voice was there to remind her that he still thought it strange that she and Robert had been standing very close, with the added intimacy of hands touching against her face.

'He lost his fiancée a year ago, Brad, and that was why I agreed to go out with him on his free evenings. But of course I couldn't after you asked me to marry you. . . .' Again her voice trailed, this time owing to the great surge of misery that enveloped her whole being as the words of Marcia swept in again. Brad had deceived her, and he had used her—yes, used her as a tool against the girl who had injured his pride so unbearably that he had wanted only revenge of the kind that would hurt Marcia the most . . . marriage to another girl. Why she was now so reluctant to keep her knowledge to herself was a circumstance most puzzling to Caryl . . . and yet . . . To reveal what she knew would inevitably create a rift so wide that their marriage could collapse—

'You were saying . . .'

Brad's voice startled her from her musings and she continued. 'I decided to tell you about his tragedy and ask if we could make him a little happier by having him to dinner. It would be something for him to look forward to.'

'He's never mentioned this fiancée. She died a year ago, you said?'

'In a car accident, and he hasn't got over it. He couldn't settle at the hospital because Mary had worked there, too, as a nurse, and so he took the post here, looking after your uncle, because, he said, it would take up most of his waking hours.' Her voice became husky with sadness as she proceeded, and she saw Brad's face relax, his expression become less taut.

'So that was why you were going out with him.'

'Not the first time. I'd been walking, and so had he; we met, and I suggested we go down to the harbour for something to eat. It was then that he confided in me, and it just so happened that it was the anniversary of Mary's death, so Robert was glad I'd asked him to eat with me.'

Brad was thoughtful, but he did not keep his wife long in suspense. 'I'm glad you've told me this,' he said.

'Of course we must invite him over.' There was a moment of silence before Brad went on. 'We mustn't let him think it's because of pity, though. He'd not like that.'

'I'll manage to explain all right,' Caryl assured him. 'And thank you for agreeing to my suggestion. He was relying on me to help him—to take his mind off his sorrow for a few hours each week. I felt terrible when I knew the outings must stop.'

'It means so much to you?' Brad's eyes were fixed on her face, an odd expression in their depths.

'To help someone is incumbent on all of us' was her quiet rejoinder.

'He was very upset when I told him of our intended marriage.' Brad's face was thoughtful as he added, still regarding her with that odd expression, 'I rather thought there had been something more between you than sympathy on your side and gratitude on his.'

Caryl ignored that, but her chin went up automatically. What right had he to throw out hints like this when his own behaviour was so open to reproach?

'I can invite him over this evening, then?' she asked.

'Certainly.' Brad looked at her across the table and said slowly, 'Robert will be out of work soon.'

'I've tried not to think of it. I kept telling myself that Uncle will not die yet.'

'He's rallied before,' mused Brad. 'This time, though . . . We shall know more when the doctor has been.' Brad's eyes seemed suddenly to burn with a strange light and he was far away from her. With Marcia? Why, chided Caryl, did she always have to bring that detestable girl into it?

'It will be awful for Robert if he's out of work at this

time. He needs to be fully occupied all the while in order to keep from brooding over his loss.'

'I might be able to find him something.'

Caryl's eyes brightened . . . and her husband's narrowed.

'You will? Oh, Brad, that is kind of you!'

He said nothing to that, and in fact he lapsed into total silence. Caryl, watching him surreptitiously from time to time, noticed the tenseness of his face, the brooding quality in his eyes, and felt sure it was his uncle he was thinking about now. The man whose days were numbered. . . . Brad would inherit everything, but Caryl knew for sure that he would rather have his uncle live on if that were possible.

After lunch Caryl went along to see Robert. Immediately he opened the door she said, 'Brad wants you to come over for dinner this evening.'

'He does?' Robert's eyes flickered. 'For some special reason?' He opened the door wider, and Caryl stepped into the hall.

'Is Uncle resting?'

'He's listening to the radio.'

'I don't want to disturb him. I just came over to ask you to come to dinner.' She looked up into his handsome face. 'You will come, won't you?'

'You'll have to explain, Caryl. Why should my employer suddenly treat me as an equal?'

'It's not sudden,' she said almost shortly. 'You've been to dinner before.'

'That was a party—'

'What difference does it make?' Robert remained silent, and she hesitated, biting her lip. 'There's only one way to explain,' she decided at length, 'and that is to tell you the truth. I told Brad about Mary and said it would be nice if you came to dinner on your evenings off. Please come, Robert,' she begged. 'I shall feel so much better if you do.'

'Caryl,' he said gently, 'there's no need for you to feel guilty—'

'I'm not feeling guilty—'

'But you are. You've been thinking that if you hadn't married Mr. Craven, then you and I would have gone out together twice a week to the café.'

'All right, you have the position straight. Will you come to the manor instead of the café? What's the difference?'

'There's a big difference. . . .' He paused because of the sudden brightness in her eyes, the convulsive clasping and unclasping of her hands. 'Does it mean so much to you?' he inquired in gentle tones, and she nodded her head instantly.

'I can't explain fully, Robert, because there doesn't seem to be an explanation other than the one I have given you. But it's very important to me that you accept. I shall be unhappy if you don't.'

'In that case, I'll accept. Tell your husband I thank him for his graciousness.'

'We dine at eight—but I expect you know that already,' she added self-consciously.

'Yes, I do know. Shall I come at eight or a few minutes before?'

'At half past seven if you can. Your relief arrives at six o'clock, you once told me.'

'That's right.'

She was happy, and it showed as she gave him a smile before leaving. 'I'll tell Brad you'll be with us for aperitifs.'

'I shall look forward to it.'

Much later, when Robert had gone back to his own part of the house, Brad said casually, 'I shall be away for the next few days, Caryl. I've some business to do in the north of England.'

'Oh . . . what part?'

'Chester,' he answered, and naturally her eyes widened in surprise.

'That's very near to the kennels where Emma and I worked—but of course you know.' He merely nodded absently, and Caryl said, 'Can I come with you, Brad? Emma leaves for Nigeria the day after tomorrow, and it would be lovely to say goodbye properly instead of over the telephone. . . .' Her voice drifted off to silence as Brad shook his head.

'Have you forgotten about Uncle?' he asked.

'No, but I'd very much like to see Emma before she leaves. I could come back without you if your business wasn't finished.' She looked at him in the silence that followed, noting his expression. It was implacable, and she knew it was futile to pursue her request further. Brad had no intention of taking her with him. For one rebellious moment she toyed with the idea of saying she would go up to see Emma anyway, but she refrained, controlling the impulse, mainly because she had no desire to cause dissension between Brad and herself. But she felt flat and dispirited for the rest of the evening. She and Brad were in the drawing room listening to classical music played on a tape recorder. The piece—Tchaikovsky's waltz from the Serenade for Strings—floated softly around the room, and until Brad had spoken she had felt relaxed and even happy because her husband had been especially charming to her and she was able to reject from her consciousness everything Marcia had said. Now, however, Caryl was beginning to wonder if Brad had been putting on an act for the benefit of their guest.

'I'm sorry about Emma,' she heard him saying, 'but I feel you should put Uncle first.'

'Yet you are going away,' she could not help reminding him, a tart edge to her voice.

'It is at his request that I am going.'

At his request . . . ? Caryl was about to say this aloud when something made her hold her tongue. For she had a strong suspicion that in his present mood Brad would be likely to tell her that it was none of her business. So she asked instead, 'How long shall you be away?'

'I'm not sure. Three or four days, I should imagine.'

'The Chester Races will be on.' She spoke to herself, reflecting on the happy hours she and Emma had spent at the races. Whenever they were on, she and her sister would try to get time off work. They both adored horses, and to go to Chester Races was something they would look forward to for months. She said presently, 'Shall you go to the races?'

'I might, if I have time—but it is doubtful,' he added as an afterthought. His voice was cool, his whole manner aloof, as far away as the expression in his eyes.

Caryl sighed, and the weight of depression made her say, in a small, deflated little voice, 'I'm tired, Brad. If you'll excuse me, I'll go to bed.'

'Tired?' He frowned, glancing at the clock. 'It's only a quarter to ten.'

'I'm tired,' she repeated and rose from her chair. 'Good night . . . I'll try to be up early so as to see you before you leave.'

She had meant her coldly spoken words to be a very

firm hint that she did not want him in her room tonight, and, knowing the depth of his pride, she would have gambled on his taking that hint. But it was his arrogance and mastery she had not reckoned with, and so, an hour later, she found herself turning from the window, where she had been staring out at the view for the past half hour after taking a bath and getting into her nightdress and négligé, and staring in surprise as her husband entered from the adjoining bedroom. She had not heard him come up, nor any movement at all, but he was in his dressing gown, and she frowned on realising he had nothing on beneath it. She spoke, asking a question even while knowing the answer. 'What do you want, Brad?'

His straight dark brows shot up a fraction, making her bristle. 'That's a strange question to ask, Caryl,' he said suavely and moved in silence across the carpet, stopping a few paces from her, his eyes sweeping over her dainty figure, absorbing everything from her flushed face to her firm, high breasts, and then farther until they rested on pink-tipped toes peeping from the soft folds of the négligé and its matching nightdress. Her colour deepened, and so did her anger.

'I did say I was tired,' she reminded him tautly.

'Yet you've been up here an hour and are not yet in bed.'

There was no answer to that, but she said quietly, 'Well, I'm going to bed now . . . and I'd rather be alone, if you don't mind.' What was the matter with her? The last thing she wanted was dissension between Brad and herself; it was for that reason she had not mentioned the scene with Marcia. Yet here she was, perversely holding out against what Brad would surely term his 'rights.' Moreover, she had wanted the marriage to become normal, was thrilled when it had done so—and far more quickly than she would have hoped. And now . . . Impatience with herself caused her to turn from him, not realising he would take it as a slight until she felt his fingers gripping her waist and she was jerked round to face him.

'It so happens that I do mind! What on earth has come over you tonight?' he demanded, tightening his grip as she began to struggle.

'It's just that I don't feel like— I want to be on my own!'

'For any particular reason?' he inquired in a much softer tone of voice.

'I've told you several times—I'm tired!' She made another attempt to free herself but succeeded only in hurting herself. Fury blazed at her helplessness, and as her eyes glittered she saw her husband's narrow.

'You didn't show any signs of tiredness while Robert was with us,' he reminded her in the same dangerously soft tone.

'Robert!' she exclaimed. 'Don't tell me you suspect me of—'

'You were damned anxious for him to dine with us,' he snapped. 'And you've a familiar way with him that I resent! You'll oblige me by remembering you have a husband!'

She could only stare, unable to believe that he could suspect her of liking Robert in *that* way! Yet she was equally unable to accept that he was jealous. He had never mentioned love, and in fact she knew he did not love her, so how could he possibly be jealous?

'I can't think of your reason for bringing Robert into it,' she said at last in biting accents. 'You know very well why I wanted him to come to dinner, why I go out of my way to be nice to him. You ought to be ashamed of yourself for these petty suspicions that appear to be troubling you!' Contempt had crept into her voice, and as soon as she saw the effect she knew she had made a mistake, gone too far.

She had no time to steel herself for what was to come before his arms were about her, her hands imprisoned and her lips crushed beneath the mastery of his. The assault was almost savage, taking her off guard, and she had no chance to resist him with her body melded to his and her hands fastened to her sides. She did try to form a barrier when he arrogantly attempted to force her lips apart, but the next moment she was uttering a little moan of pain and surrendering to his demands. His tongue was rough and warm and dominant within the dark softness of her mouth. She had no defence against the finesse of his roving hands, and soon her body was surrendering just as her lips had done.

There was no gentleness about his lovemaking, no tenderness such as that which had characterised it before. Anger was the spur to his passion, and complete mastery his aim. She had defied him, and he intended to punish her, in his own particular way. His lips left hers for a few seconds, but his mouth remained close; she could feel his fiery breath against her cheek, the pain of his hard thighs like iron against her feminine softness, and tears filled her eyes. She should never have fought him, defied him, because she never wanted it to be like this.

She said, but almost silently, 'Brad . . . don't take me in anger. . . .'

She was trembling, but if he noticed he was not in the least affected as, leaning away, he flipped a hand to the back of her neck and the négligé dropped to the floor.

The nightdress, dainty and transparent, remained about her body for a little while as Brad's eyes roved, seeing everything, darkening with passion ready to ignite.

'You're beautiful. . . .' His throaty accents reflected the passion flaring in his eyes, and he crushed her to him again, one hand sliding down her spine, the other dealing with a shoulder strap and then enclosing her breast within his warm brown fingers. She shuddered and gasped as reluctant rapture shot through her whole body, affecting every nerve cell, setting them alight with the flame of desire. 'Have you forgotten that it was you who said this relationship was to be permanent, that it was impossible, and unnatural, for us to experience the intimacy of marriage and then go our separate ways?'

His fingers were playing with the hypersensitive skin on her throat, and he smiled as she quivered against him, then hid her face against his chest. He tilted it up, forcing her to look into his eyes, while his fingers still tantalised, moving, light as thistledown, over her skin, exploring with the skill of long experience, finding the places that would quicken her reflexes, stimulate erotic nerves and desires.

She had no wish now to fight him; all her emotions were heightened and she wanted him to take her, to dominate and master her, but not in anger. And when he made to slip her one remaining garment from her warm, submissive body, she clutched it to her, saying in a pleading tone, 'Don't hurt me, Brad. I'm sorry I angered you.'

Her limpid eyes, uplifted to him in anxious scrutiny, held the appeal of a child's, and the innocence. For a long moment he looked down with a gaze that was hard. She blinked and her lips moved convulsively. He watched the twitching of the hands which clutched the transparent material of the nightdress, and suddenly his expression changed. She breathed again, a quivering sigh of relief escaping her. Brad drew her close to his heart, and his hands were infinitely gentle when at length he removed the nightdress and, lifting her as if she were no heavier than a doll, he laid her down on the bed. The light was snapped off; she felt him beside her and turned joyously into his arms.

Chapter Eight

Brad telephoned as soon as he reached his hotel in Chester. How was his uncle? he asked, and there was no mistaking the anxiety in his voice. At breakfast that morning he had given Caryl the phone number of the Grosvenor Hotel, where he would be staying. Robert also had the number, and Brad was ready to return immediately if his uncle should take another turn for the worse.

'He's about the same,' said Caryl. 'Very weak, but, strangely, he seems happy. He was smiling most of the time while I was with him this afternoon.'

'It's our marriage that has made him happy,' stated her husband without hesitation, and she had to agree.

'So everything's all right, then?' she heard Brad say over the wire.

'Yes, fine.' She gave a small sigh, conscious of the

emptiness within her, an emptiness which would be there until he returned.

Conversationally she mentioned the call to Robert when she saw him later. Sir Geoffrey had gone to bed early, and so she invited Robert to dine with her, even though he was not officially off duty. One of the maids was told to keep dropping in to make sure Sir Geoffrey was asleep, and Robert would slip away, too, though not actually during the meal.

Caryl found herself confiding in Robert after remembering he had invited her to do so if she wished. She told him of the scene with Marcia, saw his eyes widen in disbelief, and heard him say when she had finished, 'She must have been crazed with jealousy to have behaved like that! Where was her good breeding, her dignity?'

'She was venomous, Robert. It was awful. I felt thoroughly shaken and drained when she had gone.'

'I'll bet you did! I knew something had happened, but I'd no idea when I invited you to confide that it would be anything like this. I can scarcely believe she'd actually admit to saying a thing like that behind your husband's back.'

'She didn't explain how he came to overhear,' mused Caryl, and then in answer to a question put by Robert she said no, she had decided not to have it out with Brad, because it could do no good at all, but a great deal of harm.

'To your relationship?' He nodded. 'I think you were very wise, Caryl.' He glanced at the wine bottle, and Caryl asked him to top up her glass and also his own.

'James is neglectful tonight,' she said with a grimace. 'When Brad's here he's hovering about all the time.

However, it's better without servants lingering around you, isn't it?'

'You'll have to get used to it, I'm afraid.'

'I know.' She fell silent a moment as she dealt with the fillet steak on her plate. 'Emma would have fitted in far better than I,' she owned, fork poised momentarily.

'Nonsense,' he chided. 'You've adapted wonderfully well.'

She made no response, and after a thoughtful moment he said interestedly, 'Emma goes off tomorrow, I think you said.'

'Yes. I must phone her early. She catches the plane at half past one in the afternoon.'

'And you don't know when you'll see her again?'

Caryl shook her head. 'Not for a year, at least,' she predicted . . . but how little she knew. . . .

It was when they were drinking coffee in the drawing room that Robert said, 'What are you going to do about Louisa?'

Caryl's eyes glinted. 'I don't know how I'm to get rid of her, but I am determined to do so at the first opportunity.'

'Without telling your husband I can't see any way at all.'

'Telling about her carrying tales?' Caryl gave a small sigh. 'I can't do that without telling him about the scene with Marcia, and that is what I am determined to avoid.'

'So for the present Louisa stays?'

Caryl nodded. 'I've been so cold with her, though, and abrupt. In fact, Robert, I confess to being the arrogant mistress!'

He had to laugh. 'Impossible,' he stated emphatically.

'I never say please or thank you, and I *order* her to do things, whereas with everybody else I ask them graciously. But I am cherishing the hope that in being horrid to Louisa I'll drive her to leaving of her own accord.'

'It's worth a try, but she seems a thick-skinned type to me.'

'I daresay she'll stay as long as she can so that she'll be able to carry tales to Marcia.'

Robert was frowning heavily. 'It's a rotten position for you to be in, Caryl. You and—and your husband. . . .' His voice trailed.

It was the first time Caryl had seen him embarrassed. She smiled faintly and said without blushing, 'Our marriage is normal now, Robert. The holiday did it.'

'I must admit I wondered, especially after I'd seen you look so happy when you were talking about the holiday to Sir Geoffrey.' He paused a moment, then added, 'I'm glad for you, Caryl. I hope all your dreams come true.'

'And that Brad falls in love with me?'

'From the way he acted last evening I should think he already has fallen in love with you.'

'It could have been for your benefit. He doesn't know I've taken you into my confidence, remember. As far as he is concerned, everyone believes we're in love with one another.'

'Well, I still think he's well on the way to loving you, Caryl. Why, it just couldn't be otherwise, because you're so special. Haven't I already told you so?'

'You're biased,' she said with a little deprecating laugh.

'I found your sister rather special too,' he said, and it

did seem that he was far away, because his eyes had lost their positive look and were just a little dreamy.

'Emma *is* special,' she agreed, affection in her voice. 'In spite of the difference in ages we get along so well. Emma has far more common sense than I, though,' admitted Caryl with a swift grimace. 'She weighs everything up before she makes any moves. Life to her is a game of chess, and a very serious one, at that.'

'And because of this inbuilt caution she gave up the idea of marriage to Mr. Craven.'

'She knew it wouldn't work. Brad's far too bossy for her.'

'But for you? You don't mind?'

'It's the way one is made, Robert. Some women are strong, while others are poor little creatures who don't mind being mastered.'

'You're no poor little creature,' he argued with a force that took her aback. 'You're just feminine, Caryl —adorably feminine.'

She stared, nerves tingling. 'Robert . . .'

'Don't worry, dear. I'm still pining for my Mary. But I can still admire you, and flatter you if I wish.'

'You're nice,' she murmured and wanted so much to say, *and I wish you could find someone else to love, someone as nice as Mary,* but of course she did not say anything of the kind. It was not the right time, in any case; his sorrow was still too recent.

The following evening Robert was off duty, so they decided to go down to the café on the harbour. It was pleasant to be with him, thought Caryl as they took their places at the table. Nevertheless, her thoughts quite naturally flitted now and then to her husband, and she wondered what he was doing at this particular time.

Was he dining alone, or with one or other of his business associates . . . ? Her mind drifted in another direction, and she was asking herself what kind of business Brad could be concerned with up there, in the north of England. He had gone at his uncle's request, he had said.

'You're miles away, Caryl.' Robert's quiet voice broke into her musings, and she gave him a slow smile.

'To tell the truth, I was wondering what kind of business my husband would have in Chester.'

'I believe Sir Geoffrey owns some land up there. I heard him asking his nephew to sell it.'

'Oh, I see.' It explained everything, and it also brought it home to Caryl just how little she knew both of Sir Geoffrey and of Brad.

Robert said softly, almost reverently, 'Mary loved this tune; it was her number-one favourite.'

Caryl listened to the soporific lilt of the music—Brahms Lullaby—and nodded slowly.

'It's beautiful,' she said, her voice sad and gentle, her eyes misted in sympathy. 'Music always brings back memories, doesn't it?'

'I would not have it otherwise. I sometimes feel I never want to forget.'

'You never will, Robert, but time will ease the pain whether you want it to or not.'

'I want it to,' he said, but with a sigh of near despair. 'It often seems that the pain gets worse, though.'

'I think I understand, but for all that, I'm sure that every single day is a healing one. Memories will stay, but you'll eventually be able to have only the pleasure and none of the pain.'

He had been handed the wine list, but instead of

opening it he gazed steadfastly at Caryl across the candlelit table, a slow smile dawning which, observed Caryl with an access of gratification, took the shadows from his eyes.

'You're a very special person,' he murmured softly, 'no matter what you like to say to the contrary. You're the most understanding person I know.'

She grimaced a protest but made no comment, and after they had perused the menu and ordered, she asked Robert about his early life.

'I lived in Leicestershire until I was eighteen,' he told her. 'I was attending the grammar school there and would have entered university but I was suddenly needed at home when my father had an accident and became an invalid. He was a big man, and it was impossible for Mother and Elaine to manage him on their own, because everything had to be done for him.' There was a pause as Robert fell into a mood of retrospection. 'Father was in a wheelchair all day and had to be helped out at various times. Then at night he had to be settled in bed—' He broke off, spreading his hands. 'I had to get a job close to home; there was nothing else for it.'

'So you lost the chance of going to university.'

'I didn't resent anything, Caryl. I loved my father, so it was no hardship to care for his comfort.'

Caryl looked at him and shook her head. So kind and gentle . . . Making that sacrifice and never knowing one moment of regret for his lost chances.

'Your father's dead now, of course?'

'It was a happy release for him,' he answered musingly. 'He'd been in great pain for months because all kinds of other things went wrong after the accident.'

He paused, as if hesitant about adding what was in his mind. However, so much had been confided between him and Caryl that he said presently, 'I'm afraid my mother and sister are not very sympathetic towards pain and sorrow.'

'You don't get on with them?' He had so little in life, thought Caryl with a frown. It seemed all wrong that anyone as good and kind as he should be starved of love.

'We don't fall out,' he said reflectively. 'But neither are we a close-knit family. And I meant my own life to be different once I was married—dreamt of children and lots of love in my home. . . . It was so wonderful, planning a future with my Mary. . . .'

He had drifted away into the past, and Caryl made no attempt to bring him back. Tears pricked her eyes; she felt frustrated by her own helplessness, wishing she could do more to steer him over this period of heart-breaking misery.

To her surprise a smile suddenly broke over his face, dispelling the memory shadows, and she heard him say briskly, 'Snap out of it, Caryl! You're almost in tears, and that makes me feel guilty and selfish—'

'Then you shouldn't,' she chided firmly. 'I would be just the same if I lost the one I loved.'

'I think so,' he murmured and then said they must change the subject, which they did, and for the rest of the evening there was a sense of comradeship between them which neither had ever known before.

The walk home was for the most part a silent one, enjoyed by them both. The moon was argent and clear over the darkness of the sea; the endless canopy of the sky was filled with stars. A soft summer night . . . a time for romance . . . and both she and Robert in love with someone else, she with a man who did not love her, and Robert with a girl who was dead— Caryl cut her thoughts, admonishing herself for their morbidity.

'Come in for a drink,' she invited when at length they had entered the hall of the manor and Robert seemed ready to say good night and go to his own part of the house.

'You're sure—?' He stopped as Louisa appeared at the far end of the hall. She stopped in her tracks to stare fleetingly from Caryl to Robert, then moved again, towards the door beyond which was the kitchen and the servants' quarters.

'Yes,' replied Caryl, not attempting to lower her voice beyond what was normal. 'Of course I'm sure, Robert.' She called to the girl. 'Louisa, tell James to come to the drawing room!'

Louisa's mouth went tight. It was plainly difficult for her to say, 'Certainly, madam. I will tell him at once.'

'You'll not drive her away,' predicted Robert. 'Don't forget that your husband's employees all enjoy much better salaries and conditions than they'd receive anywhere else. I was amazed at what I was offered after the interview with Mr. Craven.'

'He's generous,' she admitted, thinking of the allowance he was making her. 'How, then, am I going to get rid of that tale-carrier?'

'You could be really nasty with her,' he suggested, at which Caryl opened her eyes and said in some surprise, 'But I *was* nasty with her! I always am.'

Robert had to laugh. He and Caryl had entered the drawing room, and she was already sitting down.

'You call that nasty?' With a lift of his brows. 'Well, I

suppose it was—for you. How do you suppose Marcia would go about it?'

'I couldn't be as bad as she would!'

'That's just it. As I said, you'll never drive Louisa away.'

Caryl merely sighed and let the matter drop. She supposed Louisa would tell Marcia about this evening—and Caryl now strongly suspected that the girl had watched her and Robert leave together earlier—and perhaps Marcia would relay the news to Brad. Strangely, Caryl knew no fear, nor even the merest thread of apprehension. She felt that her husband would be so disgusted at this tale-carrying that he would in fact dismiss Louisa himself, probably on the spot.

The following afternoon, when she went in to see Sir Geoffrey, she found him very quiet and withdrawn. He seemed to have an aura of resignation about him which sent Caryl's spirits right down into her feet.

'He *wants* to die,' she quivered when, after coming away, she talked to Robert in the little hallway.

'He certainly appears to be ready,' agreed Robert sadly.

She closed her eyes, totally unaware that to Robert there was a young and delicate attraction about her sadness as two great tears escaped from beneath her lids and rolled down her cheeks.

'I wish Brad were home,' she whispered. 'I think I shall phone the hotel and ask him to come back straightaway.'

'As you wish,' he said, but added that he did not believe there was any immediate danger. 'You'll remember that the doctor gave him three or four weeks—'

'But you said two. And I'm sure you're right!'

'I said it could be three,' he said, and she nodded as she remembered.

'So you don't think I ought to ask Brad to come back?'

'I don't believe it's necessary. Your husband should be back in a day or two, anyway.'

'Yes. . . . I'll take your advice and leave it—at least for today,' she said.

And as it happened Brad phoned later to say he would be back the following afternoon. 'Oh, I'm so glad! Uncle doesn't seem to want to go on, Brad. He looks to me as if he wants to die!'

'He's tired, Caryl. Don't upset yourself, dear. Try to remember that Uncle has had a good life and a long one. Some people are not so fortunate.'

She thought of Mary, who had died at twenty-one, and decided to make a supreme effort not to feel so utterly wretched about Sir Geoffrey. She was glad that Brad was coming home, though, just in case his uncle should become even worse.

It was late afternoon when he arrived, and after greeting his wife Brad went straight in to see his uncle. And whatever it was Brad said to him, it seemed to have given the old man a new lease on life.

'He's wonderful!' exclaimed Caryl when she had seen him for a few minutes before she went up to dress for dinner. 'It's like a miracle!'

'I had some good news to give him' was all Brad would say by way of explanation, but as they sat down to dinner he did advise Caryl against false hopes.

'No miracle has occurred,' he added forthrightly. 'Uncle cannot live much longer. The doctor saw him, as you know, and he saw him again this morning—'

'But that was before you arrived with the good news,' she broke in, then said no more because her husband was shaking his head.

'My news cheered him, but, as I said, it performed no miracle.'

She sighed, looking at him and as always noticing his many attractions—his striking features portrayed in deep-set eyes below strongly marked brows, the straight nose of the aristocrat, the jutting jaw and strong, determined chin. All at once she was recalling that humiliating experience she had suffered at his hands, and her attempt to prevent a blush rising was futile. Brad stared in the act of shaking out his intricately folded napkin, and at his interrogating expression her colour increased even more.

'Something the matter?' he queried.

'No, nothing.' Taking up her napkin, she shook it out and placed it on her knee. 'I wonder what we have on the menu for this evening.'

Brad's voice was edged with dry humour as he said, 'Whatever it was that crossed your mind, it was obviously an embarrassing memory.'

'It was,' she owned, deciding she would have to agree with him or lie, and the latter would scarcely carry weight when her colour was heightened like this.

'But you won't tell me about it?'

'I'd rather not.'

'You've aroused my curiosity. . . .' His voice trailed and she saw the perception in his eyes. His voice was disarmingly amused as he went on. 'The spanking, no doubt—although just why that should come back to you at this time is somewhat puzzling, to say the least.'

'You have no right to remind me of it!' she snapped.

'So it *was* the spanking. Now, what was it for? My

memory isn't serving me very well; it must be a sign of old age creeping on.'

She had to laugh then, and her embarrassment was dispelled. 'Old age,' she retorted. 'What nonsense!'

'I'm a lot older than you,' he said, taking up the bottle of wine and perusing the label.

'Eight years—that's nothing.'

'It's enough these days when men's expectations of life are so much less than women's.'

Caryl frowned and her nerves tightened. 'Don't talk like that,' she pleaded. 'What reason had you for making such a comment?'

He transferred his attention swiftly. 'I'm sorry, Caryl. I had no idea it would upset you.' His scrutiny was close, his expression strange and curious. 'There's nothing to be upset about.' Replacing the bottle, he laid his hand over hers. 'I'm sorry,' he said again. 'Forget it, my dear.'

She managed to smile, and as he watched her with an intentness she could not understand, she gradually began to wonder if he had guessed that she loved him.

When the meal was over they strolled for a little while in the grounds of the manor. Brad had said little about his visit to Chester, and because of his reticence she feared she might be snubbed—if mildly—should she ask him about it. Obviously the 'good news' brought by Brad to his uncle was not for her ears, and this she accepted, even though it was only natural that she should be curious.

'I wonder how Emma has found Nigeria,' mused Caryl as the thought occurred to her. 'I do hope she can settle.'

'Is she to be married right away?'

'Yes, just as soon as it can be arranged.' Caryl gave a tiny sigh. 'I wish I could have been at her wedding.'

'I suppose you could be there—if there's still time, and I should think there would be.'

'You wouldn't mind?' Even as she spoke, Caryl's thoughts went first to Sir Geoffrey and then to Sandy, whom she visited two or three times every day. She would squat in his cage, enticing him with biscuits or other tidbits, or she would take him in her arms and cuddle him against her chest. Avice had said he hadn't pined for her while she was away in the Bahamas, and so perhaps he was getting over his initial fretfulness—but there was Sir Geoffrey, who might die anytime. 'I don't think I'd better go,' she added before Brad could answer her query. 'I don't think I want to leave Uncle at this time.'

'Thank you, Caryl,' returned her husband simply. 'I felt I must suggest you go to Nigeria, but on the other hand I can't honestly say I wanted you to fall in with the suggestion.' He turned in the moonlight to look down at her with affection, and she felt her heart give a lurch. His attraction was just too irresistible when he looked at her like that! It gave her an urge to move very close, to tuck her arm in his and nestle her head against his shoulder. 'Why not arrange to go later, when Emma and Patrick are settled?'

'Yes, I'd like to do that,' she agreed. 'I can then take my wedding present instead of sending it as I had decided to do.' Caryl paused, going over in her mind the last conversation she'd had with her sister. 'Emma was more excited than I have ever before known her to be,' she said. 'She's madly in love with Patrick.'

'He was obviously worth waiting for,' said Brad with a hint of dry humour.

'Obviously' was all Caryl returned, for as he had spoken Brad had reached for her hand and, taking it in his, had given it a little tender squeeze. She felt her blood begin to pump unevenly through her veins, knew an eagerness to go back to the house . . . and to the big bedroom where she hoped her husband would join her. . . .

She hadn't long to wait; she heard the door open and swung round, feeling alive and warm and eager. She was in his arms in seconds, her own winding themselves around his neck, her lips offered for his taking, parted and supplicating. A low laugh echoed indistinctly through the room as he bent his dark head to accept what was offered. She did not care if he knew she loved him. For if it was true that love begets love, then it was better that he knew, because then he would not have to worry about his pride if and when the time came for him to say he loved her. Marcia intruded, like an ominous cloud shutting out the light, but resolutely Caryl dismissed the girl, for she could have no place in a situation like this.

'I wonder if you know just what an irresistible little temptress you are!' Brad's lips were like fire against her cheek, his breath swift, uneven. She felt the tempered steel of his maleness against her thighs, the slow caress of hands that were warm and gentle yet so possessive as to be arrogantly demanding and masterful. Everything about him was masterful—the strength of his kisses, the way he compelled her to arch her pliant body to the coiled-spring tautness of his own, the look in his eyes that possessed all that was primitive and inexorable.

It was a long time afterwards that, sated with rapture, torpid from an excess of love's ecstatic delights, they lay with arms about each other, bodies close in warmth and tenderness, exchanging quiet kisses before their whispered good nights were finally spoken.

A week later Caryl received a letter from a friend who lived in Chester. Lucie had been to the races and taken some snapshots.

'I'm sending a couple on to you,' she wrote, 'because I know how you used to enjoy a day at Chester Races. I was fortunate enough to know someone who knew someone who owned one of the runners, so here I am, lording it in the owners' enclosure! I'll bet you envy me, especially as I backed this man's horse and it won at twenty to one.' Caryl merely gave a cursory glance at the snapshots and then continued reading the letter. Lucie was asking about Emma and about the kennels, and last but by no means least, she said, she wanted to know how Caryl was getting along in her new life as a 'member of the aristocracy.' Smiling at that, Caryl folded the letter and laid it aside while she more closely perused the snapshots.

'They're good,' she said aloud. 'Yes, Lucie, I do envy you. . . .' Her voice trailed as, her eyes having strayed to another snapshot lying on the table by the letter she had folded, she stared in tense disbelief, every nerve in her body seeming to contract so that she felt stiff and icy cold.

'Brad . . . with Marcia . . . it can't be true. . . .'

But photographs could not lie. There in the crowd by the rail was Brad, a smile on his handsome face as it was turned to the girl at his side. But was it a smile? Distance and too many people made recognition of facial emotions impossible. But there was certainly no mistaking the fact that Brad was there with Marcia beside him. . . .

Caryl's fingers went rigid, and the snapshot fluttered away from them, onto the floor. She stared at it, emotions all awry, for she was wishing Lucie had not sent the snaps, yet glad she had because otherwise she, Caryl, would have been living in a fool's paradise, shutting her mind to all Marcia had said, optimistically believing her husband was falling in love with her, remembering his saying it could happen. But now all hope was crushed. Brad had not wanted her with him simply because he was taking Marcia. With the stilted movements of an automaton she stooped to pick up the picture, then stared at it again, fascinated by it, drawn to it, hating it.

What must she do? There was only one answer. This time a showdown was inevitable.

Chapter Nine

Caryl sat back on the couch and wondered why the lawyer and Brad had insisted on her being present at the reading of the will. She could understand why the servants were here, and she was inordinately glad to know that Robert had been considered by the man whom he had cared for so efficiently and so patiently. But for herself . . . Her eyes met Robert's, and he frowned at the shadows in their depths. She had confided in him about the snapshot—in fact, she had been forced to show it to him because of his instant disbelief of what Caryl had told him.

'It can't be Marcia,' he asserted. 'Trouble is, Caryl, you've probably had her on your mind and so you think it is her.'

She had brought out the snapshot. Shocked, Robert had nevertheless advised her to keep silent. She did not want a rift with her husband, he had reminded her. But it was something she could not keep to herself, and the result was that Brad, unable to deny the evidence of the photograph, had adopted an attitude of cold indifference—but only after he had tried to persuade his wife not to take the matter too seriously.

'There are times,' he said with quiet gravity, 'when things are not quite so transparent as they appear to be. I can say with truth that I have not been unfaithful to you.'

'Liar!' she had flung at him, pain and self-pity and a heart that wept being the force which drove her, making her blind to argument or even reason. 'You didn't want me along because you were taking her! You still love her, so why don't you be a man and admit it?' Caryl's eyes blazed in the pale frame of her face. 'I shall now tell you some more,' she went on. 'Deny it if you want, but I shan't believe you!' And she related everything Marcia had said, gratified to see both consternation and disbelief in his face.

'Marcia actually told you all this?'

'I'd not know it if she hadn't!' returned Caryl with a flash of scorn at his putting the question at all.

'I can scarcely believe it.'

'She was crazed with jealousy, and frustrated, I suppose, knowing she had brought it all on herself by ridiculing you behind your back.' Her glance raked him from head to foot; she saw his eyes narrow and smoulder, but she was past fear at this moment. All she desired was to hit back—hard. 'Well,' she challenged, 'aren't you going to deny it?'

'You know I can't deny all of it.' His eyes still smouldered, but Caryl now realised that any anger he felt was against Marcia rather than his wife. 'It's partly true. . . .' His voice fell to silence as he noticed her expression.

Her mouth quivered and her eyes shone with unshed tears. Only now did she realise just how desperately she had wanted him to deny it, to tell her it was all malicious lies . . . and yet, how could he deny it? It was the truth; Caryl had never for one moment doubted Marcia's word, for she remembered vividly both her own opinion and Robert's that there had been another reason for Brad's wanting to marry her besides the one he had given.

'It's partly true,' said Brad again, pale of face and with a nerve pulsing in his cheek. 'I did overhear Marcia ridiculing me, and I was furious—no, that's too mild a description of how I felt. I once spanked you; it was more to teach you a lesson for the future than anything else, and I had no real intention of hurting you, but with her—' He broke off, and his wife shivered visibly at the evil, savage mask that had spread across his face. 'With her I could have used my riding crop!'

'But instead you sought revenge by marrying me.'

'I've just admitted that revenge was partly the reason, but Uncle's happiness came into it as well—'

'You'd never have married me for that reason alone!' she broke in wrathfully.

'Perhaps not—'

'There isn't any "perhaps" about it! Revenge on the woman you loved—and still love—was the chief reason you married me! You used me for your own ends. It was despicable!'

'Don't try me too far,' Brad warned in a very soft tone. 'I have just said that facts are sometimes not so transparent as they appear to be, and soon I can explain several things to you.' He paused, and it did seem that although the innate arrogance was still there in his eyes, there was something else present, too—a sort of request that she be patient. 'When I say I can explain certain things,' he went on after a thoughtful pause, 'I'm referring to the evidence of the snapshot, which I believe is hurting you far more than the reason—or one of the reasons—for my marrying you.'

He sounded sincere, she thought, but so oppressive were her pain and anger that she rejected everything but her desire to hit back.

'You're rotten,' she flung at him, 'and I hate you!' She stopped and waited; he spread wide his hands and made a little sound that was a mingling of impatience and resignation. It infuriated her, but all she said was 'I want Louisa dismissed.'

'Louisa?'

'How do you suppose Marcia knew we weren't sleeping together?'

Brad's face grew dark. 'You believe she was carrying tales to her former mistress?'

'Someone provided your girl friend with the information?'

'Marcia is not my girl friend,' he snapped.

'Then why were you at Chester with her?'

'Caryl, for God's sake stop this! We shall have it out later. Now, about Louisa: it seems feasible that she was the informer, but I'd not care to dismiss her unless I knew for sure.'

'Then question her!'

'On so delicate a matter?' Brad's eyebrows lifted a fraction. He was altogether too calm, fumed Caryl. It was as if he had no real feeling of guilt over what he had done.

'I want her out of this house—at once!'

But the matter was in fact to be left in abeyance, for at that moment Robert had come with the information that Sir Geoffrey had had another heart attack.

'I've rung for the doctor,' he supplied before Brad could put the question. 'Your uncle's very bad, I'm afraid.'

For two days and nights Brad scarcely left the old man's bedside. Caryl had been in, too, but always when her husband was taking one of his brief rests. And so a chill and distant relationship had grown and flourished, and it was gradually borne in on Caryl that the marriage was a failure and must end. Now, though, was not the time to broach the subject of a separation, and in fact as the days passed Sir Geoffrey seemed to rally, and Caryl even suggested to Robert that he might continue to improve. But it was not to be, and a fortnight after the heart attack he died peacefully in his sleep.

Caryl had then tentatively mentioned a divorce and had seen Brad's dark eyes ignite and had heard him say in harsh imperious tones, 'We're married and we stay married!' And after a tense, electric pause he added, taking her by the shoulders and bringing his face close to hers, 'If the door between our rooms is locked against me tonight, I'll break it down!'

She had been far too afraid to ignore the threat; she unlocked the door which had been barred against him since her accusations had been voiced. But although she submitted to his lovemaking, she was determined not to reciprocate, with the result that he had not come to her since.

There had been nothing distinctly antagonistic in his manner towards her, though, just that cool indifference and a certain exasperation, almost as if he were dealing with a fractious child, a circumstance which both puzzled and infuriated her.

Caryl's reflections were interrupted as she heard her name—or, rather, that of her sister—mentioned by the lawyer. Until now her interest had been vague, her mind absently absorbing the fact that legacies had been left to all Sir Geoffrey's staff, and an unbelievably large one to Robert. But now her full attention was arrested. She lifted her head and her eyes met Brad's as the lawyer in his monotonous tone imparted the information that she had been left a fairly large sum of money.

But Emma was the name mentioned. . . .

'It's the money for which the land in and near Chester was sold,' Brad told her afterwards when they were in the drawing room, Brad having seen the lawyer to the door himself. 'Uncle suddenly wanted the land sold and you to have the money. I went up there to sell it for him and I was successful. That was the good news I mentioned to you.' Caryl said nothing, and after a pause he continued, 'Uncle was troubled about that land for some time before his death. It had been rented out to two separate farmers, both of whom refused to give it up on the termination of their leases. Agricultural land is always dicey as regards getting it back once you have let it, because farmers are so well protected. However, I and the agent up there finally persuaded both men to buy the land they were tilling. The price was right—' Brad spread his hands. 'You will get the proceeds when they arrive.'

'It's my sister's money,' said Caryl quietly and received a swift and frowning glance from her husband.

'Don't be absurd. Uncle left it to my wife.'

'Believing your wife was Emma.' Finality in her

voice, because she had no intention whatsoever of accepting the legacy.

'Emma wouldn't take it.'

Caryl shrugged her shoulders, a gesture which seemed to vex him, because his frown deepened. 'Be that as it may. The money, then, will go to you.'

'It will go to you,' he snapped, temper rising at her manner. 'Uncle meant it for you—the name is of no importance!'

'Your uncle believed, right to the end, that I was Emma. Most certainly he believed I was Emma when he altered his will to include a legacy to your wife.'

'I refuse to discuss the matter when you're in this idiotic mood, Caryl!' And on that he left her, anger in every step he took.

She went to find Robert. He was in Sir Geoffrey's sitting room, standing by the window, staring out across the garden to the distant rugged shoreline where at one end cliffs fell down to the sea. He turned and smiled as she entered. She closed the door and sat down.

'What is it, dear?' he asked gently, coming towards her with slow and silent footsteps.

'I'm leaving Brad,' she replied briefly.

'Nonsense, Caryl. This will pass—'

'He's in love with Marcia, so how can it pass?' Tears caused a sudden ache behind her eyes, and her throat felt dry and tight. 'There's nothing between Brad and me now,' she went on flatly when he did not speak. 'Nothing at all. He treats me with a sort of mechanical civility, speaking only when he has to.'

'I still feel you ought not to leave him.' Robert's expression was set and stern; for the first time she realised there was another side to him, a distinctly masculine one.

'We've just been discussing the legacy I was left,' she said, changing the subject. 'It was meant for my sister, and so I'm not accepting it. Brad was furious, but I don't care about that.'

'The legacy was meant for Brad's wife,' began Robert when Caryl interrupted him, almost impatiently. 'Please don't you start,' she begged. 'Brad says it was meant for me, but as far as I am concerned it was meant for Emma.'

Robert frowned and gave a small sigh. 'Best leave it for a while,' he recommended. 'Each one of us is too upset for clear thought at present, or for making decisions.' He paused a moment, and then: 'As for me—I had no expectations of anything and I feel stunned, unable to assimilate the fact that I'm almost rich.'

'You deserve it all,' she said staunchly. 'I was so happy to think that Uncle had noticed all you did for him, and appreciated it.' She looked at him as he moved towards the drinks tray and took up a decanter. 'What will you do?' she asked, a catch in her voice. 'Shall we keep in touch?'

He turned to face her, a smile on his lips. 'Can you imagine our not keeping in touch?' he said.

'No, not really.' She recalled Brad's saying he might find Robert another post when his uncle died, and Caryl wondered if he would keep to that. Of course, Robert might not want to stay, not now that he had some money.

'Will you have a glass of wine?' he asked.

'Yes, please.'

He poured it, came over, and put it on a table close to her chair. 'Don't make any decisions, Caryl,' he said seriously. And he looked directly at her as he added, 'I want you to make me a promise that you'll wait a little while—not be impulsive.'

She hesitated. Yet it was easy to make the promise, for although it was all very well to say she would leave her husband, what was she going to feel like when the actual moment of departure arrived? The pain would be excruciating.

'I promise,' she said, warmth in her voice which he knew was gratitude for his advice and his understanding.

That evening at dinner Brad said right out of the blue, 'Did you go out with Robert while I was away?'

'What makes you ask that?' Caryl faced him unflinchingly as she put the question.

'I have reason to believe that you went to the café on the harbour. I had forbidden you to go out with Robert, but perhaps you'd forgotten.' Almost harsh the tone, and his eyes were glinting.

'Whom have you been talking to, Brad?'

His fact tightened at her evasion. 'It doesn't matter. I asked you a question, and I'll have an answer, if you please.'

Her temper flared. The arrogance of him! The imperious way he spoke and looked! Had he forgotten the snapshot already?

'You wouldn't have asked the question if you hadn't already had some suspicion that I'd been out with Robert. I take it you've been talking to Miss Boyle?'

'She did phone—'

'To carry tales. And where did *she* get her information? Have you asked yourself that?'

His eyes darkened and his mouth went tight. 'Louisa?'

'Who else?'

'I'll speak to her.'

'She seems to spend half her time spying on me!' she flared, saying something she knew was not quite true—since she had no proof that the girl had actually spied on her—but her temper was to blame. How dare Brad take his wife to task for an innocent outing when he had been guilty of much, much worse? 'Louisa couldn't have known we went to the harbour café, though, so it was a presumption on your part, I suppose.'

'A correct one, it would appear.'

'Very well, it was a correct one! If you can go out with the Boyle woman, then I can go out with Robert! At least I am not having an affair with him!'

'Nor am I having an affair with Marcia.'

'I don't believe you. You stayed with her in Chester!'

'I did not *stay* with her in Chester!'

'I believe you slept with her!'

Brad's eyes narrowed darkly in the taut frame of his face. 'Do you realise what you are accusing me of?' he asked in a dangerously soft voice.

'Infidelity!'

'Without proof?' he shot back with such disconcerting sharpness that Caryl found herself blushing painfully.

'I admit I have no proof,' she returned in a much-subdued voice. 'However—'

'However nothing! Don't start qualifying, Caryl,' he admonished, his tone sharp as steel. 'You've admitted you've no proof; let's leave it at that, shall we?'

'You puzzle me,' she complained. 'I wish I could understand you.'

His narrowed scrutiny was searching and long. She saw a slight frown cross his brow, saw him open his mouth, then close it again, as if biting back the words he would have liked to utter. She shook her head, profoundly conscious of indefinable currents in the air and of her own tensed waiting . . . for what?

James entered to say Caryl was wanted on the telephone. She asked to be excused and left the room. When she returned her husband started up and sprang swiftly across the floor; he caught Caryl in his arms just as her legs threatened to give way beneath her.

'It—it w-was Emma—Patrick's—dead. . . .' Her eyes were great pools of misery in the ash-grey pallor of her face. 'It—it was in a—a sailing accident. Emma was with him—oh, Brad, why did this have to happen to my sister!' She clung to him with frantic strength in her fingers, spoke with the wild incoherence of near hysteria. 'She's at the—the airport, on her way home. She'll be—be here at—at seven in the morning.'

A week had passed since Emma had arrived at the manor. Robert in his great compassion took complete charge, for Emma was in a state of collapse when Brad and Caryl picked her up at London Airport and drove her down to Dorset. And she had been in bed ever since, with the doctor attending her and Caryl, almost as grief-stricken as she, sitting with her almost all day. But Robert's was the strength that hovered over the bedroom where Emma lay; his was the command that would send Caryl off to bed when he decided she had had enough.

'She hasn't eaten a thing,' moaned Caryl, tears running down her cheeks. 'She'll die, Robert—I feel she's given up the will to live!'

He nodded in agreement, but there was no sign of

lost hope in his eyes. He knew from experience . . . oh, how well he knew! thought Caryl and felt that if anyone could save her sister it would be Robert.

He sat with her when Caryl was resting, and it was he in the end—after days of infinite perseverance—who finally managed to get Emma to take some nourishment.

'I'm giving everyone so much trouble,' Emma said one day to Caryl. 'I must try to be braver than this, for I'm sure Robert is heartily sick of looking after me!'

'He chose to do it, darling,' said Caryl soothingly. 'He insisted on taking over a task which I wanted to do.'

'He's understanding, Caryl. It seems as if he knows and appreciates my every thought, my every emotion. It's like . . . telepathy or something. It is certainly beyond my comprehension—the way he talks of my feelings, my agony of mind. . . .'

'Shall I tell you why?' asked Caryl gently.

'You mean, you know why he has this almost miraculous understanding of my feelings?'

'He lost his fiancée just over a year ago,' explained Caryl. 'And so now you know why he possesses this infinite understanding. Robert is something very special, Emma, and you'll soon be feeling grateful that he hadn't already left here when you arrived.' She explained about Robert's legacy and said that, with the acquisition of a comparatively large sum of money, it would have been understandable if he had decided to leave the manor and make a home for himself.

'I hope he won't leave yet,' said Emma huskily. 'I seem to rely on him so heavily—' She looked apologetically at her sister. 'You don't mind that I feel this way—drawn to Robert—do you, Caryl?'

Caryl leant over the bed to hug her, and it was a moment or two before she could speak, so emotionally affected was she both by Emma's words and her own great surge of love towards her sister.

'You know I don't mind. I'm glad, because I know that Robert will be good for you at this terrible time in your life.'

Emma nodded her dark head. She had always been so strong, thought Caryl, but now she seemed helpless, almost totally dependent on Robert.

Caryl often thanked him for what he was doing, but he always shrugged off her gratitude.

'I feel so contented suddenly,' he confessed, a far-away look in his eyes, as though he were endeavoring to understand himself. 'I'm thinking about Emma all the time, where once it was Mary who constantly intruded into my mind. It seems that what I do for Emma is so positive; she needs me even more than Sir Geoffrey needed me—' He broke off, spreading his hands. 'I suppose it must be because she is young, with all her life before her, whereas Sir Geoffrey's life was fast coming to its end. There was nothing I could do for him; with your sister there is so much I can do.' Resolutely he stared ahead, his gaze once again far away. 'I know I can make her live again, Caryl, and do you know . . . it sometimes seems to me that Mary would want me to help Emma to—to live. . . .'

Caryl swallowed something hard and painful in her throat. She had always said that Robert was special, but he was more than special; he was the angel who would support Emma in this tragic time, who would save her from total despair.

'You are not thinking of leaving us for a while, then?' She knew the answer, but somehow she had been forced to ask the question so that her mind could be easy.

'Not while Emma needs me,' he answered without hesitation.

She looked at him, at the wide, compassionate mouth, the open gaze, the handsome lines of his face—marred a little these days by anxiety. 'She depends on you absolutely, Robert,' she murmured at length. 'She needs you far more than she needs me, and that is strange, because we've always been so close,' added Caryl reminiscently.

'You don't mind?' Robert looked curiously at her. 'There's no feeling of resentment that Emma prefers my ministrations to yours for most of the time?' It was blunt speaking, but between him and Caryl the bond of friendship had grown so strong that exception would not be taken, and they both knew it.

She shook her head. 'I'm only too grateful to you, and you must know it, Robert.'

'Yes, I know it. And I shall not fail either you or your sister,' he added resolutely. 'It'll take time, but, as you once so wisely said to me, dear, every day is a healing day.' And as if by some mutual agreement he and Caryl moved towards one another. His arms came about her as hers likewise came about him, and they kissed as if to seal a bargain.

Both turned as Brad came into the room. His dark eyes smouldered, but all he said was 'I want to talk to you, Caryl. I'll be in my study in a quarter of an hour's time.' And with that he swung on his heels and left as silently as he had come.

Robert was frowning heavily. 'That was unfortunate.' He sighed. 'I ought to have called him back to explain.'

'There's no need,' she returned flatly. 'I told you, there's nothing between Brad and me now. I can't even begin to discuss a separation at present, with Emma as she is, but later—' She broke off to swallow the hard little lump that had risen in her throat. 'A divorce is inevitable. I must tell him so.'

Yet even as she said that she was thinking of what Brad had said about being able to explain certain things which, he implied, were not what they had seemed. He was referring to the fact of Marcia's having been with him at the races, and now she came to think about it there had been times when he had seemed to be on the point of telling her something which she sensed was important. Resolve would give way to indecision, and following this his manner would become aloof, distant, impersonal. Yet he would appear to be affected by some deep emotion, his face softening, his eyes taking on a brooding look that was almost akin to unhappiness.

'I don't believe a divorce is inevitable,' she heard Robert saying gently. 'So much has been happening, dear—what with Sir Geoffrey's death and all it entailed afterwards, then this tragedy of Emma's— Everything will sort itself out in time, dear; I feel sure of it.'

'I wish *I* did,' sighed Caryl, wondering what her husband wanted her for in his study. 'I had better go.'

'If he mentions that little scene just now, then don't be too proud, or too angry, to explain,' was his advice as she went slowly to the door.

Chapter Ten

Brad did not immediately mention the scene, as Robert described it, but spoke about the legacy left to her by his uncle.

'I have explained about the name, and the lawyers are in agreement with me that the money is rightfully yours. Uncle left it to my wife.'

'Who he believed was Emma, the girl he thought so much about when you were engaged to her years ago.'

'Caryl,' he said with some asperity, 'don't be so obstinate! You know as well as I to whom that money belongs!'

'Apart from anything else, Emma could do with some money at this time. She'll not be able to work yet awhile.'

'I could shake you,' returned her husband softly. 'I don't suppose for one moment that your sister would accept the legacy.'

'I can persuade her—or Robert can if I fail. He has tremendous influence with her.'

'And with you, it would appear—or perhaps influence is not quite appropriate. Are you in love with him?'

She flinched at the razor sharpness of his voice and had no idea what made her say, 'I refuse to answer a question like that.'

He said slowly, appearing for some reason to have difficulty with his words, 'You have given me an answer.' He stood up and, turning his back on her, walked to the window and stood with his hands in his pockets, staring out across the terraced garden to the severe line of Lombardy poplars and the serried bar of cypress trees to the south. Beyond them could be viewed the vast expanse of sea, its swell rolling towards the rock-strewn scimitar of the bay, cresting into a voluminous curtain of spray as it approached the shore, then smoothing out in its progress on the beach. Gulls swooped and glided, playing with the air currents; Caryl could almost hear their cry echoing against the cliffs.

'I know it isn't the right time,' she began, driven by some compelling force she could not resist, 'but I think you'll agree that a divorce is the only solution to our problem.'

At that he swung around, the snarl on his lips almost animallike in its viciousness. 'Forget a divorce! You're my wife, and it stays that way!'

'With you in love with someone else?' Her voice was steady, but her heartbeat was erratic, as were her nerves. 'Uncle's dead now, so there's no need for us to stay married—'

'Nevertheless, we do stay married.'

The fury in his eyes ought to have been warning enough, but Caryl foolishly ignored it as she flashed, 'Do you suppose I'm the sort of spineless creature who'll be willing to lie passive while her husband indulges in an affair with another woman? What sort of a life would that be—either for you or for me? Marry her and be done with it! You can't resist her, but you're not man enough to admit it—' She broke off as he leapt towards her making for the door, but she was not quick enough.

A cry of pain and protest fell from her lips as Brad grasped her by the wrist and swung her hard against his body. She fought, but to no avail; her head was forced back and her husband's mouth clamped down on hers in a kiss that lacked both gentleness and respect. Vainly she struggled, gasping for breath as he took his fill, moistly possessing her mouth, compelling her lips apart, while his hands slid right down her spine to find soft curves and make her aware of his maleness as she was brought so close it seemed her whole pliant frame was melded to his. Her breasts were flattened against his chest, her hands pinioned to her sides. She was helpless, and it infuriated her; she called him a savage when at last he freed her mouth.

'Savage, eh!' he gritted, eyes smouldering as they looked down into hers. 'You've seen nothing yet! There'll be no more of this platonic, unnatural situation! You'll resign yourself to being my wife—do you understand?'

For a moment she was too shaken to speak, and she felt that the whole of her body was bruised. Tears started to her eyes and, chagrined, she felt them falling onto her cheeks.

'Tears for what?' he rasped. 'Robert?'

'If you must know—yes!' she cried, pushing against his chest and managing to free herself from his slackened hold. She stared at him from the other side of the room, her face drained of all colour, her chest heaving, her small hands clenched at her sides. What had she said? Tears for Robert. It was a senseless thing to say, because it did not explain anything. Surely her husband would realise that. But he was too angry, too incensed, to dwell on what she had said, to take time to analyse it. With another swift movement he had her prisoner again, this time to take her firmly by the shoulders and shake her unmercifully.

'Robert! Well, wife, you can forget Robert, because he goes from here at once! He's sacked!'

'No!' Caryl stared at him aghast, forgetting the pain he'd inflicted, ignoring the fearful throbbing of her heart as she said imploringly, 'You wouldn't do that, Brad! Emma needs him, desperately! Oh, I beg you—don't send Robert away!'

His eyes were implacable, merciless, as they looked down into hers. 'Using Emma, are you?' he sneered. 'Well, it won't work! You can care for your sister just as well as he—better, in fact. It will keep you out of mischief!'

'You're unjust!' she flared, small and pale before him but with the courage to add, 'I hate you—do you hear me? I hate you for your duplicity in continuing to have an affair with Marcia, and I hate you for your cowardice in—'

'Cowardice!' he thundered, reaching out as if he would shake her again but then letting his hands fall to his sides.

'Yes, cowardice! You'd send Robert away solely because you're afraid that he and I—'

'Be quiet!' he lashed, eyes like live coals in the angry frame of his face. 'If you throw your affair with Robert at me again, I shan't be responsible for my actions!'

She backed away, saw the sneering amusement enter his eyes to mingle with the fury blazing there. She was again wondering what had come over her, goading him like that by mentioning Robert in the kind of way that would cause Brad to assume she and he were having an affair. Suddenly she wanted to laugh, yet the next moment she was fighting back the tears. How had a situation like this come about? Both she and Brad had lost control, driven to lengths they never would have believed possible. She had said she hated her husband, when in reality she loved him with all her heart—had loved him since she was eighteen years of age. Yet, driven by anger and jealousy and several other emotions, she had allowed her tongue to run away with her. Too late now to attempt to undo the damage.

'If you don't mind,' she said very quietly, 'I'll go to my room and lie down.'

'We haven't settled this thing about the legacy.' His voice, too, was quieter, and it seemed that most of his anger had dissolved.

'I have told you how I feel, and that ends the matter. No one can force me to accept the legacy.'

'You damned stubborn wretch!'

'Just one thing,' she said as she moved towards the door. 'If you send Robert away, then I go, too.'

'You—!'

Caryl turned at the door, her hand resting on the ornate brass knob. 'Call it blackmail if you like, but I mean what I say.'

She went out, half fearing her husband would prevent her from leaving. She felt her heart heavy as lead within her as she made her way upstairs. She'd had to make that threat in order to ensure that Robert would stay and look after Emma.

And now Brad must be in no doubt at all that there was something between his wife and Robert, she thought miserably. Entering the room, she flung herself on the bed and wept as if her heart would break.

What was to be the end of it? Brad was so adamant about a divorce, and the more she dwelt on this the more she was forced to accept that she could have made some drastic mistake in assuming he was having an affair with Marcia . . . yet how could she explain away the evidence of the snapshot?

'But a snapshot doesn't prove he was having an affair,' she murmured between her sobs. Brad had reminded her that she had no proof; she had admitted it and then in her anger forgotten it again.

The following day she talked at length to Robert after having been over to the kennels to see Sandy. Emma was sleeping when she went into her room, so she tiptoed out again and went to seek Robert.

'Did your husband mention my kissing you?' he asked before Caryl could speak.

'Yes. He's of the opinion that we're having an affair.' She spoke casually, easily, as always when she was talking to Robert, for there was no need to hold anything back. She felt it must be a unique relationship and wished her husband could understand it.

'I see. . . .' Thoughtfully and with an unfathomable inflection in his voice. 'You denied it, I suppose.'

Caryl shook her head reluctantly, aware of the warm

blood in her cheeks. 'I was angry,' she explained briefly.

'You didn't deny it?' Robert stared at her incredulously. 'But, Caryl, why not? It was the logical thing to do!'

'I wasn't capable of logic at the time. I was in a temper.'

'You wanted to hit back—' Robert drew an exasperated breath and looked sternly at her. 'You had better go along and explain,' he advised. 'Or perhaps I had better do it.'

'No, Robert, I'll do it—but later. I'm not in the mood just now. How is Emma this morning?'

'She was awake for most of the night. I sat with her and we talked. I decided this morning at five o'clock that I had better give her a sleeping tablet. I don't like giving them to young people, but it seemed to be a necessity on this occasion.'

She looked at him, examining his face, and now realised just how tired he looked. 'You ought to get some sleep, Robert,' she suggested. 'I'll keep popping into Emma's room, and as soon as she wakes I'll stay with her.'

'Will you, Caryl? Then I think I will go to bed for an hour or so.'

'Is there anything I can do for you?'

'Only one thing,' he answered gently, 'and that is to go and talk to your husband and explain about us.'

Easier said than done, mused Caryl as she stood on the terrace and stared out over the bay. The sun was brilliant across the sea, shining on the red and white sails of luxury yachts, on the smaller boats coming in with the night's catch, and on the beach itself where children played or searched about in rock pools, making discoveries that caused them to dance with delight and make urgent signs for their parents to join them.

Everyone so carefree, while here, in this great mansion, heartache and dissension reigned, with only Robert seeming to be normal.

Resolutely she turned and went along to her husband's study. 'I want to have things out with you,' she stated almost before she was through the door.

'Indeed.' Coldly, as Brad tossed down his pen and leant back in his chair, presenting an autocratic figure which made his wife draw a long breath and decide to count ten before she spoke again.

'About Robert and me—'

'If that is all,' he inserted arrogantly, 'then I'm busy!' And he took up the pen again and started to write. Caryl closed the door and moved closer to the desk.

'There is nothing between him and me,' she persevered, glancing at the vacant chair but hesitating about taking possession of it.

'That's not what you implied a little earlier.' He seemed indifferent, although there was a hint of derision in his tone, not unmingled with scepticism. Obviously he was not willing to believe her when she said there was nothing between Robert and herself.

'I was in a fury,' she returned on a slightly sullen note. 'You—you goaded me into saying things that weren't true.'

Again he put down his pen, slowly this time, as his eyes took on an expression of interest. Deep-set and probing, they caused her some discomfort, and she averted her head in order to avoid their piercing scrutiny.

'You stated quite categorically that your tears were

for Robert—because you couldn't be with him all the time, no doubt.'

'That's an assumption,' she retorted, lifting her face. 'And it happens to be a wrong one!'

'Perhaps,' he invited in a soft voice, 'you will come to the point.'

'I have. I came to tell you there was nothing between Robert and me.' She was subdued, feeling inadequate—inferior, almost.

It never occurred to her that her manner would set her husband's thoughts travelling on an altogether wrong track until she heard him say evenly, 'You've been talking with Robert this morning, obviously. He heard from you that he was to lose his job, so he sent you back to me to attempt to put things right by telling me a pack of lies. . . .' His voice trailed as the colour drifted into her cheeks. 'And it's not an assumption this time,' he went on coldly, 'because your blushes give you away. What exactly did Robert tell you to say to me?'

'He didn't tell me to say anything—except to explain what is the truth.'

'Well, you've wasted your time and mine, because I don't believe you.'

Caryl's temper flared in spite of her resolve to remain calm. 'Please yourself! Do you suppose I care whether you believe me or not?' She strode to the door and flung it open. 'I still mean what I said about leaving if you dare to send Robert away!'

'I shan't allow you to blackmail me,' he threw out as she turned to go. 'I shall see him today and dismiss him without notice!'

'Are you paying him anything?' she challenged and saw his mouth go tight.

'Are you suggesting I stopped paying him immediately after my uncle died?' he questioned icily.

'You'd said you might find him another post, but you didn't.' She was on the defensive, aware she had said the wrong thing but too angry to admit it.

'He has a post, looking after Emma.'

Impatiently she shrugged and went out. She made her way to the kennels, went in, and picked Sandy up and held him to her breast. Robert found her there; from his bedroom window he had seen her striding away from the manor and guessed her interview with Brad had been anything but cordial.

'He says he's going to dismiss you,' she quivered. 'And it's all my fault, Robert, for making him believe we were having an affair.'

'Are you sure you made him believe that?'

'Of course I'm sure. Why should he want to send you away if I hadn't convinced him?' Robert remained thoughtful, and she added almost impatiently, 'You're so calm about it, Robert. What will my sister do without you?'

'No one is indispensable,' he returned quietly. 'However, I am not as pessimistic as you, Caryl. I have never known your husband to be unjust, and it would certainly be unjust were he to dismiss me without affording me the chance of explaining. Even Louisa was given an opportunity of defending herself.'

Caryl nodded, remembering that although Brad was almost as convinced as she that Louisa had been carrying tales, he had had the girl sent to his study and given her a chance to deny the offences. She had broken down and admitted to carrying tales to her former mistress. And even then Brad had paid her a full month's wages in lieu of notice, which, under the circumstances, he had no need to have done.

'I don't know why you're not furious with me.' She looked at Robert with regret in her eyes. 'It was so stupid of me to mislead Brad into thinking there was something between us.' She put Sandy down and looked at his paw marks on her blouse. 'It won't be long now before he goes back to his mistress,' she murmured rather absently as the thought came to her. 'At least someone will be happy.'

'We shall all be happy eventually.' Robert smiled, beckoning her to come out of the cage. When she was beside him he took her hand in his and gave it a reassuring little squeeze. 'I shall go and see your husband at once—'

'Oh, no, he isn't in the mood to listen!' she broke in urgently. 'I think you had best leave it—'

'Nothing of such importance is best left alone,' he interrupted in his usual calm and quiet voice. 'If I have to go, then I'd rather know at once.'

'I can't understand why you aren't mad at me—' Caryl shook her head from side to side. 'Don't you see, it's all my fault? If you have to go, then I'm entirely to blame! And poor Emma—what is she going to—to do without you?' Tears were gathered in a tight little cloud behind her eyes, but she managed to hold them back. She withdrew her hand from Robert's and said resignedly, 'Go, then, and see if he'll listen.'

'I am quite sure he will,' Robert assured her, then paused a moment, smiling down at her. 'Cheer up, child. You look as if all the troubles of the world are about to descend upon you!'

'I love him so,' she said tragically.

'Then why in heaven's name don't you tell him? I'd have credited you with more sense than to keep it to yourself all this time.'

'Tell him, when he doesn't love me?' Caryl's mouth went tight. 'Not likely!'

'If he doesn't love you, then why is he jealous of me?' was Robert's softly spoken question as Caryl fell into step beside him when he turned away from the kennels to direct his footsteps towards the manor.

She stopped and stared up into his face. 'Jealous?' she echoed. 'Brad isn't jealous of you!'

'Then perhaps you can explain why he's so anxious to get rid of me?' he inquired equably.

Caryl blinked, endeavouring to clear her mind, because at present she was quite incapable of straightening out thoughts which had become tangled by what Robert had just said.

Jealous. . . . Was it possible? Something trickled along her spine.

'Marcia,' she said swiftly. 'What about her?'

'You, my child, have had that woman on the brain far too long! It was all over and done with when Mr. Craven married you—'

'The snapshot!'

'Has he never tried to explain about that?'

'He said he would, later, but he never has.'

'There's still time.' Robert quickened his pace until Caryl was trotting to keep up with him. 'Is your husband in his study?' he asked when they had reached the front door of the manor.

'He was when I left him a quarter of an hour ago.'

'You go and see how Emma is. I'll join you in a little while.'

* * *

Emma was sitting up in bed; she looked brighter than Caryl had seen her late last night, and she guessed the drug administered by Robert had done its work well.

'How are you, darling?' Caryl sat down on the end of the bed, trying not to think about Robert and what was taking place in her husband's study. 'You've more colour than you had yesterday.'

'I feel better in myself, much better.'

'Can I get you anything?'

'I'd love a drink of something sharp—lemonade?'

'Coming at once!' Caryl rose, went down to the kitchen, and got the drink herself.

'You know,' said Emma as she took the glass from her sister's hand, 'I am lucky, really. I could have been on my own at this time—'

'Not on your own,' corrected Caryl at once. 'You'd have had me, at least.' She paused a moment, and then: 'You haven't told Father, and you ought to, dear.'

'It was no use upsetting him. Besides, I couldn't have stomached that woman he married. He'd have insisted I go there, and there'd have been friction if I'd said no, which I would have done. I'll wait awhile and then tell him.'

'He doesn't even know you're back in England.'

'Well, don't tell him. I'd love to have him come and see me, but he'd not come without her.'

'I have to agree.' The woman was so possessive that she would never allow him to come down to Dorset alone, especially to see his daughter. Both Caryl and Emma had long since realised that their father's wife was jealous of his daughters and there was nothing they could do about it. It had been a relief to all four of them when the two girls had found themselves jobs away from home.

'How's Sandy?'

'Great. And he's over the hump now; it'll not be long before he's going back to Miss Haldene.'

'Just to think . . . if you hadn't come here because of Sandy, you'd never have married Brad. Isn't fate strange?'

'Unfathomable,' briefly and with a tinge of bitterness which Emma failed to notice, much to her sister's relief.

'And me. . . . Why did Patrick have to die?' Emma's whole body shook, and Caryl took the glass from her trembling hand.

'Don't think about it, darling,' begged Caryl even while wondering how Emma could help thinking about it. 'You were saying, love, that you were—well—fortunate in that you have people around you at this dreadful time. Robert is so concerned about you—'

'Robert is wonderful,' broke in Emma and the ghost of a smile actually touched the dry outline of her mouth. 'He says I'm to get up tomorrow and he'll walk with me in the gardens.'

Caryl looked at her curiously. 'You don't mind being told what to do, then?'

'Not by Robert. He isn't bossy like Brad—only firm.'

'Can't see the difference myself,' mused Caryl, and then, after a pause: 'I'm glad you're getting up, though. The weather's glorious and the gardens must be at their very best. Soon we shall have autumn here, and then everything will begin to fade.'

'Yes. I must try to enjoy the rest of the summer. . . .'

A sob caught her voice, and Caryl caught her to her breast, speaking soothingly to her, stroking her cheek and her hair. Emma, who had always been the strong one, was now desperately in need of comfort and of the strength of others.

'Where is Robert?' she asked, drawing herself away eventually.

'He's with Brad at the moment, but he won't be long.'

'I think I'd like to get up today—but I had better wait until he comes, hadn't I?'

'I think you should—' Caryl turned swiftly as the door opened and Robert stood there, looking grim, and yet there was a hint of amusement in his eyes as well . . . and something else. Satisfaction? He thumbed, an action so alien to him that she gave a slight start. He was indicating the door.

'Your husband wants you,' he said. 'I shouldn't keep him waiting if I were you,' he added by way of advice.

'Why? Is he—I mean . . . ?'

'Definitely not in the mood for pandering to any whims. In fact—' Robert lowered his voice to a mere whisper as she passed him. 'In fact, you'll be lucky if he doesn't beat you . . . and I'd not blame him.'

'Robert, what have you said—' Her question was cut off as he gave her a little shove. She found herself outside the door and heard the firm, decisive click as the catch fell into place.

Brad was by the window, and it was some seconds before he turned to face his wife. Her eyes sought his across the room; she noticed the inflexible set of his mouth, the dark, stern quality of his eyes. He frowned at her approach and afforded her a sort of cool attention. Not a very propitious start, thought Caryl, not without a little access of misgiving. Decidedly uncomfortable under the cold steel of his glance as it swept her slender figure, she coloured delicately, profoundly conscious of the low cut of her dress, revealing the thrust of her firm, enticing breasts. She pushed a hand through her glowing hair, just for something to do, because the silence was far too trying.

'Well,' he said at last, and as if compelled by his eyes alone she moved forward into the room. 'Close the door,' he ordered, and she turned at once to obey.

'Robert,' she began hesitantly, 'er—he's been speaking to you, hasn't he?'

For answer there was nothing more than a swift, impatient drawing of his breath as he pointed to a chair. 'Sit down,' he commanded. 'Don't stand there as if you expect to have your ears boxed any moment!'

She bristled, lifting her chin. 'Robert said you wanted to see me. Please tell me what it is about.'

The steely eyes glinted and his mouth went tight. 'Be very careful,' he warned in a soft voice. And then, as she sat down: 'What the devil did you mean by leading me to believe you were having an affair with Robert?'

'I believe I have already explained,' she answered, injecting a haughty note into her voice even while her nerves were all awry because there was no doubt that her husband looked almost ready to murder her. 'You made me angry, and I spoke in revenge—to get my own back!'

'I ought to make you smart!' he declared between his teeth. 'To get your own back, eh? And did it afford you any satisfaction?' he wanted to know, folding his hands now and moving to lean against a white marble column supporting the mantelpiece.

'You asked for it' was Caryl's pettish rejoinder. 'If you could have an affair with—'

'Careful,' he warned again. 'There was no question of my having an affair with Marcia any more than there was of your having one with Robert. And you know it!' he added grittingly.

'Brad,' she said on a little pleading note, 'what are you trying to say to me?'

'Do you mean to say you don't know?' The change in his voice and manner was so sudden and unexpected that she gave a little start, her big eyes staring into his across the width of the room. 'Come here,' he ordered softly and held out his arms to her.

'But—'

'Caryl . . . I told you to come here. . . .'

Rising slowly, she moved towards him, then stopped some small distance away. 'It—it seems I've made a mistake—'

'*A* mistake!' The new softness deserted his eyes momentarily. 'One mistake? That's an understatement if you like!'

'The snapshot . . .' Caryl looked pleadingly at him and spoke in a strained little voice. 'There's some explanation, obviously?'

'I said there was.'

'But you didn't explain.'

'I intended to, but when you seemed to be in love with Robert I changed my mind.' His eyes flicked over her. 'I told you to come here.'

She moved towards him again, felt him take her shoulders, felt too the piercing scrutiny of those dark, metallic eyes, and saw the censure and impatience within their depths. But there was something else as well, and it caused her heart to leap even though she told herself he could not possibly love her.

His arms came about her; his lips closed on hers. But it seemed mainly automatic; he was still impatient with her, and censorious. Stung by his manner, she tilted her chin, and her eyes took on a sparkle of militancy and protest which made his gaze narrow and his hands tighten almost painfully on her shoulders.

Nevertheless, he began to speak, to explain the reason for Marcia's being with him in Chester. She had somehow gained the information that Caryl had married Brad when the real bride should have been her sister.

'Marcia wouldn't say how she had come by the information,' continued Brad musingly. 'I do not doubt that we can blame Louisa, though; she must at some time or other have heard you addressed as Emma by my uncle—she went in to clean his rooms at times. And as most of the other servants were here when I was engaged to Emma, a little subtle questioning on Louisa's part would put her in possession of certain facts which would interest Marcia. Marcia asked me if I would take her to Chester, and of course I said no. Then she threatened to tell my uncle of the deception, and I was forced to agree to her demands. . . .' His voice trailed away, and his wife gave an involuntary little shiver as she noted the almost savage expression which crossed his face. 'All the same,' he continued on a stern inflection as his eyes met those of his wife, 'she did not have the power to make me sleep with her—as you intimated!'

Caryl averted her eyes as colour swept into her face. 'I'm sorry,' she mumbled almost inaudibly. 'I—I ought not to have jumped to conclusions.' And she added before he could speak, 'But neither should you have jumped to conclusions as regards Robert and me—' Her words were cut off by the little shaking she received.

'There's absolutely no comparison! You practically admitted to having an affair with Robert—'

'But previously I'd denied it!'

'So had I denied having an affair with Marcia. If my memory serves me correctly, you called me a liar.'

She bit her lip, looking guilty and contrite. 'I'm sorry,' she said again and moved away, to stand by the open window through which the zephyr of a breeze was blowing, carrying flower perfumes into the room.

'Robert assures me that you love me.' Softly came the words, and spoken with confidence. 'And as I love you, there seems no sense in this divorce you spoke of.'

Caryl swung around, heart beating overrate. 'You—love me?'

'Don't look so darned surprised' was his impatient rejoinder. 'I said in the beginning that we'd very likely fall in love one day.'

She took a faltering step towards him. 'You don't love Marcia . . . ?' Caryl's voice faded and she took a stragetic step backwards as she saw her husband's eyes kindle.

'I've just said I love *you!*' he snapped.

'Well, there's no need to be so bad-tempered about it,' she complained, and then, as if by common consent, they both burst out laughing. 'Oh, Brad, how did it happen?' she was asking breathlessly five minutes later.

'It was bound to. How could I be married to the most wonderful girl in the world and not fall in love with her?' His voice was tender and low against her cheek, his caressing hand warm and possessive at her waist. 'I wanted to tell you—several times I tried—but always it seemed that you cared for Robert. I kept thinking of the truism that pity is akin to love, so it was not much comfort for me to tell myself that it was pity you were feeling for him.'

'It was pity, but—but . . .' Shyly she hid her face in his coat. 'I've loved *you* since I was eighteen, Brad. I later believed it to have been a crush—you know how young girls are with older men? But when you asked me to marry you, I knew for sure that there was love on my side.'

'I guess there was love on my side, too,' he returned reflectively. But then he shook his head. 'I don't truly know. I believed I was still in love with Marcia, but after I'd overheard her speaking so disparagingly about me I would never have married her, no, not even if you had not come along.'

Caryl snuggled close and said after a while, changing the subject, 'The legacy, Brad. I think—'

'That you and Emma should share it. It's large enough for you both to have a substantial sum, and I think you will agree that Uncle would like it that way if he could but know.'

'That's a very good idea,' she returned enthusiastically, for although she would far rather her sister have the lot, she knew her well enough to be sure she would never accept it. 'Brad . . . do you suppose Robert and Emma might one day . . . get together?'

'Nothing so sure' was Brad's firm assertion. 'It won't be yet awhile, but I'm sure we shall be having another wedding here. I was thinking that they could have the forest lodge. It's been standing empty for years and needs modernising inside. You and I shall give it to them when they become engaged; they can use their legacies to renovate it, so they'll not be feeling they're receiving charity—I imagine both have rather more than their fair share of pride. If Emma wants to take over the kennels, she can, because otherwise I intend closing them—'

'You do?' she broke in urgently. 'But Sandy?'

'I'd not close them until all the dogs have gone back to their owners. However, I rather think that Emma might like to take them over, because, after all, they did originate as my uncle's hobby. As for Robert, well, I am sure I can find him a post—maybe as bailiff.'

'Farm manager?'

'Estate manager. I feel sure he'll like it just as well as looking after sick people.'

'You're so good, Brad.' She would have nestled close again, but he put a finger beneath her chin, tilted her face, and, bending his head, kissed her tenderly on the lips.

'Love me always, my darling,' he murmured, his breath warm and clean on her mouth.

Her eyes, soft as a fawn's yet dark with tender passion, looked steadily into his. 'For as long as I live,' she returned simply and pressed her body very close as her husband's arms tightened around her.

Coming next month from *Silhouette Romances*

Strangers May Marry by Anne Hampson

Only Paul could help Laura keep her adopted child, but in return he demanded marriage! Was his price too high, or could Laura find true happiness married to a stranger?

Run From Heartache by Brenda Trent

Summer had lost her memory in the accident that brought Bracken into her life. But the past could never diminish her desire to share the future with this loving man.

One Man Forever by Juliet Ashby

Winging her way toward Paris with her new boss, Penny wondered if she could handle the job, and more importantly, could she handle the autocratic and devastating Pierce Reynolds?

Search For Love by Nora Roberts

He was suspicious, jealous, demanding and impossible! So why in heaven's name had Serenity lost her heart to her French cousin, Christophe, Count de Kergallen?

Island On The Hill by Dixie Browning

Frances had worked hard for her independence, and she wasn't about to give it up for a man. But rugged, handsome Cabel was more than a man—he was a lover!

Arranged Marriage by Brittany Young

Analisa had married Rafael Santiago out of respect for her dying father. But she hadn't anticipated the scorching flame of his love under the reddening Spanish sun.

READERS' COMMENTS ON SILHOUETTE ROMANCES:

"I would like to congratulate you on the most wonderful books I've had the pleasure of reading. They are a tremendous joy to those of us who have yet to meet the man of our dreams. From reading your books I quite truly believe that he will someday appear before me like a prince!"

—L.L.*, Hollandale, MS

"Your books are great, wholesome fiction, always with an upbeat, happy ending. Thank you."

—M.D., Massena, NY

"My boyfriend always teases me about Silhouette Books. He asks me, how's my love life and naturally I say terrific, but I tell him that there is always room for a little more romance from Silhouette."

—F.N., Ontario, Canada

"I would like to sincerely express my gratitude to you and your staff for bringing the pleasure of your publications to my attention. Your books are well written, mature and very contemporary."

—D.D., Staten Island, NY

*names available on request